and FOUR

books by Charlotte Paul

AND FOUR TO GROW

THE CUP OF STRENGTH

MINDING OUR OWN BUSINESS

GOLD MOUNTAIN

HEAR MY HEART SPEAK

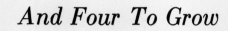

And Four To Grow

to GROW

Charlotte Paul

Random House / New York

To three men

. . .

Eᴅ, Hɪ, *and* Jᴏʜɴ

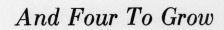

And Four To Grow

1

I AWAKENED RELUCTANTLY, keeping my eyelids closed as
if such a childish evasion would fool both me and the
world. The last impression of the night's dreams disin-
tegrated into tiny bits, hung still for a moment like insoluble particles suspended in a glass of water, and then
settled to the bottom of my mind. Sleep had deserted me.
Even the warm confusion of half-sleep had abandoned me
to the reality of a new day.

Slowly I opened my eyes and looked around the room.
Why this senseless feeling of uneasiness? The twin bed
next to mine was empty, but that wasn't unusual, for my
husband often went to work at five or six o'clock in the
morning and the alarm clock said ten minutes to seven.
Apparently he'd had a bad night. His pillow was on the
floor, the bedding had been pulled out at the bottom, and
sheets and blankets were in a tangle. Sleep had been hard
for him, waking was hard for me. Why?

Years ago I invented a way of combating the vague,

harassing feeling that "something is wrong." Not an original system, I'm sure; something like it has probably been in general use ever since man reached such a high level of intellectual development that he knew how to worry. Ignoring an undefined worry never seemed to reduce the worry; often I found that defining it did. The trick was to ask myself bluntly, "What's bothering you?" and once in possession of the answer, to continue with "What else?" and if necessary, "Isn't there something more?" until finally I'd dug down to the fear I hadn't previously faced or forgotten.

Warm in my cocoon of bedclothes, I again closed my eyes. Whatever was distressing me today couldn't be important. We'd had five hard years after we bought the weekly newspaper and printing plant in Snoqualmie, Washington, but after eight years we were well established and business was good. Our two sons were healthy and had completed a full month of the fall term without attracting the critical scrutiny of the grade school principal. We lived in a comfortable home on a corner of an old homestead where a four-thousand-foot mountain loomed over the meadow which was our front yard. The scenery was beautiful, and so was the thought that everything was paid for—the house at the foot of the mountain, the plant four and a half miles to the west in the town of Snoqualmie, and the two automobiles with which the publisher and his wife raced from one to the other.

True, my New England forebears would not have considered us "well off" because we had little or nothing in the bank. But I was born in Seattle, and Ed in Billings, Montana, so we measured money in terms of what we could earn in the future rather than in what we had saved in the past. Ed's efforts had tripled the gross income of the *Snoqualmie Valley Record* and I had been doing well as a free-lance writer, so by our definition we were well off and could prove it in tax statements and canceled mortgages if not in conventional forms of legal tender. In short, our worries appeared to be over. But I was lying in bed on a bright new October morning, reluctant to wake up, dreading the day.

Of course there was our Open House in observance of National Newspaper Week. In the backshop, presses and Linotype machines were to be running. Coffee and cake would be served on the editorial desks of the front office. In the side room, we would show a documentary film guaranteed to tell the weekly newspaper publisher's story so movingly that many of our guests would hurry to the reception desk to pay up their overdue bills.

Had I ordered enough cake? That was a specific worry, but it was neat and housewifely. In the same sense I was "worried" about the chairs. Our guests would expect to sit down while they viewed the film. In eight years Ed had purchased all kinds of expensive equipment, especially during periods when we had the least money, but he'd never gone overboard for chairs, probably because they don't have motors.

The undertaker had solved the problem by offering to lend us the folding chairs from his chapel and had even volunteered to haul them himself, but the passing of a revered old-timer had complicated the plan. If I really wanted to fret, why not try to predict whether the helpful mortician would get through with the funeral (*and* the hearse) in time to bring the chairs. . . .

I threw back the covers and sat up. These were such little, surface things. Deeper was a worry that seemed to be growing with every day I kept it to myself. The simple movements of sitting up and getting out of bed reminded me of it. My hip hurt. It was a small, dull ache, not worth mentioning to a man who had suffered two nervous heart attacks and three painful bouts with shingles.

Ed had always ignored his own illnesses, refusing to let

me call a doctor right up to the point where he blacked out or was in such pain that he literally could not speak. On the other hand, a temperature of 100 was reason to summon a doctor to the house (if the thermometer had been in a mouth other than his own) and he turned pale when I nicked my finger with a paring knife.

A little pain in the right hip, a pain so elusive I couldn't say exactly where it was coming from—no, I was right in saying nothing about it to Ed. The three busiest months of the year were just ahead, and our Linotype operator, a key man in our production line, was talking all too warmly about how things were back in Chicago.

Besides these special problems, Ed shared the concerns of all men "in business for themselves"—worries about taxes, government regulations, labor problems, and the ever increasing pressure from the behemoths of Big Business. He was not of a temperament to take them lightly. He didn't retreat before pressure, he fought it. He didn't curtail production when we were short-handed, he did the work himself. And the greater his success, the harder he drove himself, because each time he took one step forward he moved his goal two steps ahead. If I were to make a pointless reference to this little pain of mine, his burden of worry might become dangerously heavy.

And I wasn't really ill. On the contrary, I'd always been so strong that my own mother once compared me to a Percheron; affectionately as she expressed her figure of speech I knew she was thinking less of thoroughbreds than she was of horses. She was right, though, for I hadn't consulted a doctor in fifteen years of marriage, with the exception of the routine connected with Hi's birth in 1944 and John's in 1945. Other women called me remarkable because I wrote professionally, worked at the newspaper, and took care of a home and two children. "I don't know how you get so much done!" was praise I

6

valued highly. Yet last week fatigue had overwhelmed me so suddenly I hadn't been able to finish a magazine article on time, the first deadline I'd missed in seventeen years of writing. . . .

I stood up, went to the window, and looked out on the pasture to the north of our house. In a happier mood, I would have picked up the ornate little opera glasses my Boston grandfather gave me and studied the field for any signs of wild life. Deer often graze there; I've seen a coyote lope across the open meadow, porcupines lumbering toward the woods, and countless ring-necked pheasants and hawks and crows and meadowlarks. But that morning of our Open House party I was looking inward.

I had peeled off the top layers—the silly little worries about the cake and the chairs, the larger but far from urgent question of an unidentified pain and a general feeling of fatigue. Now I had reached the core of my uneasiness, and I knew it as surely as if iodine, washing painlessly across my hand, had suddenly found a break in the skin. The night before, Hi and John had had an argument with their father.

It hadn't been the loud voices that bothered me, for the course of our family life had not always run smooth. Our sons were admittedly less than perfect and their parents were not abnormally patient or wise. Like all families we'd had periodic scoldings and many a scene of the kind parents call "a family discussion" but their children instinctively recognize as a bawling out. The reigning authority—Mother, when the children were young, but in recent years, more likely Father—simply cracked down, and the boys accepted it, tearfully, philosophically, or guiltily, as the case might be.

What then was so different about last night's "discussion"? Why this lingering aftertaste? Reluctantly, I identified the roots of my uneasiness.

One was the nature of the argument. No offense had been involved, no rule broken, unless there is a precept that twelve- and thirteen-year-old boys must not disagree with their fathers. They had disagreed, and then clung stubbornly to their right to do so. A difference of opinion had grown into a two-sided argument such as adults have with other adults, and suddenly Father was no longer the reigning authority, but simply a man whose views differed from their own.

Ed had been baffled, then angered, by a relationship he couldn't accept, and I had tried to help. Here, under everything else, lay the most painful sore. In the past, we had been united in all issues concerning our children. Last night, we had been at odds. Not openly. Neither of us had admitted that I opposed him, and that he resisted, and resented, my joining the argument. But a new conflict had been born. Puzzled, cut off from each other, we had done nothing to resolve it.

The issue had arisen over our Open House, especially the backshop exhibition of printing machinery in operation. Ed's plan was that John would watch the Kluge, an automatic job press, while Hi would be stationed nearby at a larger press called a Kelly B. To contrast modern equipment with the old-fashioned, manually operated press, Ed would take his station at the "hand snapper."

"But Dad," Hi objected, "I won't have anything to do."

"Sure you will. Keep an eye on the Kelly, be ready to turn it off if a sheet sticks or runs crooked. People will come by and ask questions. You'll have to explain the operation of the press and probably a lot of other things besides."

"I don't know much about the Kelly."

Ed grinned. "More than they will."

It struck me that the jobs assigned were not being received with the enthusiasm Ed had expected the boys to show. It wasn't long since they had squabbled over the privilege of turning an automatic press on or off. To have sole responsibility in the presence of two or three hundred adults who were bound to look on them as mechanical geniuses if they did nothing more than flip the switches—what more could a seventh- and an eighth-grader ask? But Johnny's face showed no boyish delight, nor did Hi's. They were looking at each other in silence, obviously trying to decide which one would speak up.

The older boy took the initiative. "Dad, the point is, we won't actually be *doing* anything."

John hurried to support him. "All we can do is just turn them on and turn them off. If anything really happens, like a sheet going in crooked, we have to call for you."

"Of course you do. That's one reason I'm going to stay right near. We'll all be working together."

Mothers are equipped with radar systems which pick up even distant warnings of trouble between their husbands and their children. Mine recorded, faintly but distinctly. "You'll have fun," I said brightly. The moment the three words were out of my mouth I realized how silly it was to say them to teen-age boys who had just rejected their father's proposal because it offered "fun" and nothing else.

Hi turned to me. "The thing is, John and I already planned what we'd do at the Open House."

Johnny nodded. "We were going to fix up a special exhibit of North Bend Printers, Ink. We were going to print some bookmarks and give one to everybody who comes."

North Bend Printers, Ink had come into existence two or three years earlier when an ancient proof press was turned out to pasture. Rather than sell it, Ed had turned the press over to Hi and John, and completed the company's holdings by throwing in three or four drawers of worn hand-set type, a brayer or ink roller, and odds and ends of paper stock.

Ed looked thoughtfully at his sons. "I thought we'd all work together at the Open House, as a family, the way we have ever since we bought the paper."

As a family, working together—for years that had been the foundation of our existence, both in business and at home. Hi and John had been active partners since they were four and five years old. They had slept at the print shop, eaten at the print shop, worked at the print shop.

School had relaxed the bonds of this close relationship and in a sense success had divided us, too, for after a year or two we could afford to hire an associate editor who did so much of my work that I was able to stay home every morning and write. But "together" and "as a family" were still the secret words. I guessed from Ed's restrained manner that he was disturbed at having to restate them.

"You boys know that most of the printing we turn out is done on the Kelly and the Kluge," he explained carefully. "So if you do nothing more than watch them, and maybe say a word or two about them when visitors ask what they're for, you'll have a real part in the Falls Printing Company's production line."

Hi burst out, "Dad, we were going to show people our *own* printing company!"

That was where the pleasant after-supper conversation became an argument. Reduced to its bones the question was absurd: Would Hi and John operate an old proof press in the southwest corner of the building or would they stand next to two automatic presses at the north end of the building? But the conflict couldn't be so reduced. There were those two words which our sons seemed to be repeating so often these days—"our own." A "printing company" of their own, a job of their own, and for the

Open House, nothing more than a corner of their own. What we had here, Ed and I, was a battle between the "our own" of the younger generation and the "together" of the older, and if there was anything absurd about it, it was only that neither of us had seen it coming.

Foolishly, I turned my back on the question and concentrated on keeping the peace. "Ed, there wouldn't be a 'North Bend Printers, Ink' if it weren't for you. You provided all their equipment, right down to the pencils and the printers' aprons."

"Of course I did. I've also spent a good many hours teaching them to use it."

"Well, then, you've encouraged them. You shouldn't blame them for wanting to exhibit these things at the Open House."

Tight-lipped, he replied, "It isn't a question of blame."

Johnny's face brightened. "You mean it's okay for Hi and me to make the bookmarks?"

"Certainly."

So the immediate question was answered. But they had gone on talking. Anxiously promoting harmony, I broke in from time to time.

"Ed, really, I think you're misinterpreting Hi's meaning."

"I don't think so."

"I can see your point. But on the other hand, I can understand the boys' desire to . . ."

He cut me off. "If you will allow me, Mom, I'll finish what I was saying to the boys."

I caught my breath, and for several minutes held my tongue. But there was that persistent and compelling need to smooth everything out, and soon I forgot the indignant tone of voice and unusual harsh emphasis on the word "Mom," and I spoke again. "Hi, John, your father is trying to tell you that you've always been . . ."

"Mom," Ed interrupted brusquely, "if I haven't been able to make it clear to them, there is no point in going over it again."

Eventually the boys went to their rooms—rooms of "their own," I thought unhappily, and Ed and I had retired in a strange, uneasy silence. So the new day was beginning under the cloud of last night's differences. The tangled blankets, the pillow lying on the floor, killed any hope that Ed was less aware of the conflict or less disturbed by it than I.

It was such an old story. The young buck against the old buck—often as I'd watched deer on the meadow outside our bedroom window, I'd never witnessed the ancient battle. Now, I thought ruefully, it's going on right here in the house. What am I to do?

"Make some coffee," I said out loud as I reached for my robe and slippers. My usual schedule had been revised because of the Open House. Rather than writing from 9:00 A.M. until 1:00 P.M., I planned to spend the day on final preparations. Check with Grandma Bookter's bakery. Phone about the chairs. See the Methodist minister about borrowing the eighty-four-cup coffeemaker. Set up the projector . . . Gratefully I turned to my long list of little problems, and thus, for the moment, forgot the big ones.

But I could not bury the memory of the sudden, unreasonable anger that had tightened my husband's mouth as he said, "If you will allow me, *Mom* . . ." How often, I wondered, do I call him "Dad"? Where have we lost Ed and Charlotte, and the silly, affectionate nicknames we invented eighteen years ago and thought we would use forever?

ii

By holding Open House we were observing one of the Snoqualmie Valley's hallowed traditions. There are the gay Silver Wedding Anniversary Open Houses, and the more dignified Golden Wedding Open Houses, the participants' capacity for riotous living having decreased somewhat with the years. There is Open House when a new store is completed, and Open Houses for its first, second, third or twentieth year in business. Our schools have Open Houses; even playgrounds and athletic fields have Open Houses, where there are no houses at all.

During our first three years as owners of the Falls Printing Company and publishers of the *Record*, we'd been in no shape financially to treat anyone even to free coffee and doughnuts, the basic requirement of the simplest Snoqualmie Valley Open House. There was another reason why we hadn't invited the community to come in and look us over.

The original plant purchased in October of 1949 was a frame structure forty feet long and thirty feet wide. Within six months Ed had built an addition which was considerably larger than the thirty-three-year-old box to which it was attached, but his desire to equip our company with the very latest printing equipment was always one jump ahead of the number of cubic feet we had to put it in. Even after this first expansion there wasn't room for an Open House unless we brought guests in single file and led them through the shop like highway patrolmen taking cars over a difficult detour.

At the end of three years Ed had launched a major building program. We soon had a brand-new one-piece Falls Printing Company, three times the size of the one we'd bought.

"We'll have a party," Ed then announced. "An Open House celebration."

We had both been working seven-day weeks and twelve-hour days. This was standard for Ed, but not for me, and five hours' sleep never puts me in a party mood. "What's to celebrate?"

"Opening the new building. Our first three years in business for ourselves."

Three hundred and fifty guests had signed the register during that Open House in 1952. This second party in observance of National Newspaper Week was to be a cut above the first. Not as big as Open House at the Weyerhaeuser lumber mill, nor as fancy as the golden wedding parties where all the male guests wear neckties and the hostesses serve three-tiered cakes, crescent-shaped sandwiches, and other foods with social standing based on the fact that they are obviously very difficult to prepare. But we were to have a motion picture, and thanks to the undertaker, plenty of chairs. We could offer two kinds of cake cut into nice big pieces and served with plenty of real coffee—real, indeed, for it was to be made by two loggers, the husbands of members of our editorial staff, and the brew they considered fit was strong enough to send a high climber to the top of a Douglas fir without his spikes on. We even had souvenirs, for as they had planned, Hi and Johnny set up their own demonstration of "North Bend Printers, Ink" and an hour before the party began, were turning out scores of sticky, lopsided, but cost-free bookmarks.

Last-minute preparations were in full swing when the telephone rang and the clipped nasal voice of the long-distance operator asked, "Is this the office of the *Snoqualmie Valley Record?*"

I would have answered sensibly if the mortician had not pulled up to the curb just then with the load of folding chairs. I had been disturbed by the sight of the boys working "on their own" and as far from their father as they could get; the last-minute arrival of the chairs unleashed a great, bounding sense of relief. Confused by two strong emotions, I mumbled politely into the receiver, "The hearse just came. I'll go get my husband."

14

By the time guests arrived Ed had soothed the long-distance operator, the mortician had set up the folding chairs, and the local pharmacist had been drafted to run the projector. Two or three dozen subscribers were watching the presses and Linotype machines in operation and many more were seated in our impromptu motion-picture theater when a man named Joe Strout charged into the front office and asked grumpily, "What's all this?"

"Open House. Come on in."

"I'm not interested in no party. I come on business."

"Yes, of course . . ." I led him back to the front desk.

"I want to buy a want ad." He corroborated this statement by thrusting a thick hand into his trousers' pocket and coming up with eighty-five cents.

It wasn't much. Enough to pay for seventeen and a half minutes of our Linotype operator's time, or two weeks of mine. But still it was money on the barrelhead, a good omen for our Open House and for the beginning of our ninth year in business for ourselves.

I knew Joe only slightly, his wife Betsey somewhat better; as I handed Joe a pad of classified ad blanks and a pencil, I couldn't help reflecting that Betsey still owed us eighty-nine dollars for printing we'd delivered to her six months before.

Joe shoved the pad back at me and threw the pencil after it. "You write it down."

Pencil poised, I asked, "Real Estate? Lost and Found? Personal?"

He nodded vigorously. "Yeh, that's the one. That last one. Personal."

"What would you like to say?"

He growled "I'm not going to pay any bills run up by Mrs. Betsey Strout. Signed Joe Strout, Snoqualmie, Washington. I gave you the money." And with that he wheeled around and headed for the door.

"Mr. Strout . . ."

He stopped and squinted over his shoulder.

"Mr. Strout, that isn't the—well, the conventional form. Persons in your situation . . ."

"How would *you* say it?"

I replied stiffly, "*I* wouldn't. But the usual form is: 'I am no longer responsible for debts incurred by anyone other than myself.' Then your name."

"That's fine, that's fine. I didn't know exactly how it went but I figured that for eighty-five cents you could write it."

"Glad to help . . ." My voice trailed off as I studied the coins through which the Falls Printing Company had just exchanged eighty-nine dollars for eighty-five cents, with my expert assistance, of course. Wistfully I added, "Mr. Strout, your wife doesn't happen to be independently wealthy?"

The gentleman guffawed. "She hasn't got a cent, the bum!" Then he went through the door.

I watched Joe Strout's striding figure as he hurried across the vacant lot to the main street. The lawyer's office and two beer parlors were open evenings, and my guess was Joe planned to patronize all three of them.

"Don't mind him," said a woman at my elbow. "He'd skin a flea for the hide and the tallow."

I laughed. "You know him?"

The woman nodded sagely. "*And* her. My family moved here in 1917 when they built the big lumber mill. You live in this town as long as I have, you get to know everybody, and you're related to half of them."

Her eyes traveled around the room and came to rest on Hi and John, still busily rolling out bookmarks on their proof press. "Your boys are sure growing up. I got a kick out of what they said to me just a few minutes ago. They said they used to work for their father but now they've got their own printing company." She chuckled. "I like that name. North Bend Printers, Ink. I—N—K."

The argument of the night before leaped from its hiding place at the back of my mind. "They do have what they call their own company," I said woodenly. The soreness was still there, not the least bit healed by a full day's attention to cake and folding chairs and motion-picture projectors. "My husband gave them the equipment and taught them to use it. But they still work with us, of course. As a family."

She patted my arm. "They're growing up, they're changing. It's only natural they should be thinking about being on their own."

Those words again . . . "This company of theirs is all right," I said, as if the case of boys vs. father had to be argued before this grandmotherly judge. "But their interest in it probably won't last long and actually they can learn a lot more about the printing trade by working with their father as they always have."

"They're growing up," she repeated, smiling at me as if she knew something I didn't know and thought best not to tell me.

"Hi is only thirteen years old and Johnny just had his twelfth birthday."

"I know, dear," she said gently, "I know . . ." Still smiling, she moved toward the coffee urn and I heard her say to another guest, "This is a real nice place we got here . . ."

All evening the shop was crowded with so many people we did know that we assumed anyone who wasn't "local" had come with someone who was. But when the last little group said good-by and left, we realized that the stranger still lingering by the coffee urn had no such home-town attachment.

Ed approached him, extended his hand, and said,

"Sorry I didn't introduce myself earlier. I'm Ed Groshell. You're from out of town?"

"California," the man replied. He was a big man, six-feet-two or more, with big hands, wide shoulders, a large hooked nose and a general look of abundant health and prosperity. He explored his inside coat pocket with thumb and forefinger and produced a card. "My name is Harvey, Frank S. Harvey," he said, handing the card to Ed. "Like to talk to you after everyone's gone."

Ed's friendly grin held for a second or two and then gave way to a puzzled frown. "Do you mind telling me the nature of your business?"

"That's what I came to do. But you might want to keep it private."

Curiosity is an antidote to fatigue. It was 10:30 at night, and for Ed the day had begun at 5:30 in the morning, but after a moment's hesitation he said, "Make yourself at home, Mr. Harvey. The people who've been helping us tonight are just getting ready to leave. I'll be with you in a few minutes."

Coffee chefs, cake cutters, printers and pressmen and other volunteers gone at last, Ed and I returned to the man from California.

"Do you have friends in the Snoqualmie Valley, Mr. Harvey?" My intention was to be hospitable, but I sounded like a customs inspector asking for a passport.

"No. I heard about you two and your paper from a friend in Seattle. I came out tonight to look the town over. Figured on seeing you tomorrow but the first four people I talked to mentioned the Open House, so I decided I'd better look in on it."

"Look the town over?" Ed asked. "Are you thinking of going into business in the Snoqualmie Valley?"

The big man laughed. "I own some orange groves, Mr. Groshell. Never strayed very far from oranges although

I do have a little real estate here and there. No, I've got enough to do in California, but my son hasn't. He graduated from college three, four years ago. He's working for me but he doesn't like it; he studied journalism and what he wants is to buy a newspaper. Your place for sale?"

For a second Ed stared, and then he began to laugh. "No, Mr. Harvey," he said, shaking his head. "No, the *Record* is not for sale. Not now, not ever."

"If you've got a good property, I'll make you a good offer."

Hi and John were at the washbasin, rubbing kitchen cleanser onto their inky arms. With a nod in their direction, Ed replied, "Do you see those boys over there? They were only four and five years old when we bought this paper, but they've worked right along with us from the first day we came. Eventually they'll take over."

The man from California shook his head slowly. "That's what I said when my son was a boy. Then he went off to college and studied journalism. Well, you definitely set against selling?"

The door behind us opened. On the threshold were two little children, a boy about six years old and a girl perhaps a year younger. October nights are cold in the Snoqualmie Valley; if it isn't raining or blowing, gray, wet fog collects in the low places and lies heavy on the meadows. Yet these children were barefoot, and neither of them had a coat or sweater; their hair looked ragged as their clothes and their faces were dirty. I had seen them many times, for they were often out in the street.

The boy took his sister's hand and advanced, pulling her behind him. With large serious eyes, he asked me, "Is this where they're giving away the cake?"

"Come with me," I said quickly. "We've got lots of cake, right over here."

The editor of a weekly newspaper has a large file of

names where her mind ought to be, and suddenly the name of these children's parents slipped into place. There were older sisters and brothers, and younger ones, too. I'd heard of them from the man who owned the little neighborhood theater, for every Saturday night there were three or four of them left in the theater when he wanted to close up. Their parents deposited them at seven o'clock when the first show began, even youngsters so small that the tops of their heads were lower than the backs of the theater seats. By 11:30, when the last show ended, they were usually asleep, and after the owner of the theater had turned off the orange pop cooler and cleaned out the popcorn machine he had to inspect each row of seats to be sure he'd found them all. Once he'd awakened them, he faced a dilemma.

He couldn't bring himself to leaving the cold, sleepy huddle of children on the street in front of the theater. Should he make a tour of the taverns and rout out their father and mother? Should he wait a half-hour until the taverns closed and the parents would come get the children? Or should he put the children into his car and drive them home, knowing that if he did, even once, this complete baby-sitting and taxi service would be his forever after?

We had set up a few card tables near the coffee urn. Spying the tables, the children hurried across the room and quickly climbed onto the folding chairs. I filled two plates with cake, and after a glance at their hands decided to bring them forks. They accepted the plates solemnly, hesitated a moment about the forks and then picked them up.

The little boy looked up at me. Still solemn, but a little troubled, too, he asked, "Is this where they're giving away coffee, too?"

I looked at their small pointed faces and thin necks. "Do you really want coffee?"

"Yes."

"Both of you?"

"Yes."

So I poured two cups of hot, strong, loggers' coffee, and brought it to their table with the sugar bowl and a bottle of milk. Their mouths were full, but they both thanked me.

The man from California had been watching us. When I came back he said, "Good thing those two didn't show up while your other guests were here."

Ed bristled. "That wouldn't have made any difference."

The man's eyebrows went up. "Kids like that aren't much better than beggars. You might have had a hard time keeping them out."

"I wouldn't have tried to," Ed retorted furiously. "Why *shouldn't* they come in?"

It was time for a wife to rush in. "Mr. Harvey, you were saying . . ."

Without seeming to move at all, he turned toward me; your husband, the gesture said, is a crackpot idealist, so I'll talk to you even if you are a woman. "I believe I was asking if you are definitely set against selling your newspaper."

I nodded. "We are."

"You have my card," he said, still addressing himself to me. "If you change your mind, let me know."

"Yes, thank you."

There was a stiff series of farewells and handshakes and the man from California left.

"Who was that, Dad?" Hi called across the room. "What did he want?"

"He's a jerk," Ed snapped. "A big snobbish jerk. No wonder his son doesn't want to go in business with him."

Hi and John came across the shop, both of them squinting at the business card in their father's hand. "Did he say he wanted to buy the shop?" Johnny asked.

"He owns orange groves. Probably doesn't know a blame thing about newspapers."

Johnny looked at me. He was sure to repeat the question, and it was just as clear to me that Ed was irritated by the boys' interest in the stranger's offer to buy. "Finish washing up," I said. "It's late."

"You told him you weren't interested, didn't you, Dad?"

"That's exactly what I told him. Not now, not ever. The Falls Printing Company is ours and there'll be no change of ownership until Mom and I are too old or too beat to be useful and then we'll turn it over to you."

"It's very late. . . ." Both boys glanced at me quickly and then turned and went back to the washbasin.

Frowning, Ed read Mr. Harvey's business card once more and then thrust it into my hand. "Here, you throw it away."

"*Me* throw it away? If you don't want to keep it, why don't you tear it up and throw it away?"

"That's what I like about you." The frown disappeared and he broke into a grin. "Along about midnight you remember you're a lawyer's daughter."

"I'm not trying to cross-question you. I just wonder, if you *really* have no interest in selling—I mean, perhaps subconsciously you want to keep the card, but you need to feel that I approve of your keeping it, so you gave it to me. Now you're waiting to see what I'll do with it."

"It must be midnight. The lawyer's daughter has just turned into a psychiatrist."

I laughed, and he laughed with me. Together . . . Impulsively I moved toward him. Without a word he put his arms around me and held me very close, his cheek against mine. I wasn't sure what he was thinking. The same things that had been worrying me all day? I had an impulse to ask, "Why were you angry with me last night?

Why did you resent me?" I would ask him, yes, we'd have to talk about it. But not now, not right now.

"Very successful Open House," I murmured. "No complaints except from the man who said we should have had door prizes."

From somewhere above my left ear he said, "We'll have them next time."

"Already planning another party?"

"Not for next year, but October, 1959 will be our tenth anniversary. We should hold Open House then."

"That's two years from now. So much for Mr. Frank S. Harvey."

"Yes, so much for Mr. Harvey. Let's go home."

Just before we left I opened a drawer in Ed's desk and dropped the business card in with unanswered letters and penciled memoranda he'd written to himself. I couldn't tell whether he saw me do it, for he and the boys were engaged in a three-way, standing-up wrestling match. Punching and tugging, laughing and breathing hard, the young bucks and the old one were trying each other out. But the punching was easy, the tugging was affectionate. I sighed. This day was ending happily. Perhaps I had no reason to worry about my sons and their father. Certainly I should forget that there had been an unspoken issue between their father and me. Forgotten, it would surely cease to exist.

2

THE OWNER of a small business is spared the ponderous labor-management issues of Big Business, but he has one chronic help problem: he can seldom afford to hire as much help as he needs. As for "employee relations"— ah, yes. From the moment he buys the place, his relations are employed, at least those who don't object too loudly to working for nothing. In the case of the Groshell family and the *Snoqualmie Valley Record,* the publisher's unsalaried labor pool numbered three: his wife and his two sons.

When they were too young to go to school, Hi and John were old enough to sweep floors, to convert scrap paper into saleable scratch pads, and to sort out, according to length, the "slugs" or strips of metal used in most printing operations. As they grew older, they added new jobs to their repertoire. At seven and eight, they took accurate telephone messages, sold classified ads, and handled three or four jobs in the bindery department without any supervision. By the time they were nine and ten years old they could monitor the automatic presses and had memorized the position of hand-set type in the California job case or compartmented type drawer so they were able to "break down" the pages of last week's edition.

Our home life was shop life; we lived at the *Record* office. We rode to work together. We got out a newspaper together, and if it had been a hard day at the office our children didn't have to be warned to keep their voices down; they had been right there when it was hardest. Even when both boys were in school and I was spending part of the day at home, this intense side-by-side relationship continued, for it was renewed over the week ends, during vacations, and often after school. The term "partnership" was not window dressing. Our jobs were tailored to our abilities, but they were all necessary, even the little ones.

I was working at home one beautiful July afternoon when a wealthy Seattle woman called on me. Eventually she asked, "Where are the boys?"

I explained that they were at the shop with their father.

"Really? Such a nice day to play out of doors. But they will be home soon. . . ."

"Maybe, maybe not. They left at five o'clock this morning, but a big order has to be finished by tomorrow. They'll work until it's done."

"Really!" she repeated, with emphasis.

I assured her it was true, and shocked her even more by admitting that this slave labor had been drafted every day for two weeks.

She looked at me curiously, struggled for the right thing to say, and finally asked politely, "Are they both interested in the newspaper business?"

"They're interested in eating," I replied, "and they also like a comfortable home and some spending money and other things provided by the newspaper shop they're working in today."

"My son is at camp for the summer. Perhaps when he's sixteen or seventeen, some sort of a job would be educational . . ."

"I'm sure it will be." With some difficulty I kept myself from asking why her boy had to wait so long to start his education. "Hi and John are going to camp, too, for two weeks next month. We pay half their fees, they earn the other half."

"My goodness," she murmured. "Don't you want them to grow up to be happy, normal boys?"

"No," I said. "We want them to grow up to be men."

My caller left soon, but that bit of conversation haunted me for days. My children were spending long hours in a print shop while hers was outside playing games. Mine were learning the relationship of work to leisure, hers was protected from knowing there was any connection between the two. Who was underprivileged—her son, or mine?

If we were wrong, then so were many other parents in our Valley. Two of Hi's and John's grade school classmates were making the daily milk route with their father, alternating so that every day one boy worked in the barns and the other rode in the truck. Another boy changed linen and scrubbed floors in his family's motel. Luckiest of all were our friends who owned a restaurant—they had four girls, a skilled waitress-dishwasher team.

I thought of another couple with boys the same ages as Hi and John. Theirs was a family-owned tire retread shop. The father made the retreads, the mother covered a long route from service station to service station, collecting old tires and delivering the finished jobs. Now she was carrying a baby, but she still drove the truck; the boys rode with her and did the lifting. Undoubtedly they would have preferred to be playing baseball or going fishing, but they had an interest in the business *and* in the coming baby. Surely this was not incompatible with being "healthy, normal boys"?

The answer came a few days later, and not from the inner recesses of my parental conscience but from the boys themselves.

I had written a book called *Minding Our Own Business* and in it described the sometimes desperate, sometimes joyful moments of our first five years as owners of a weekly newspaper. It brought us many letters, most of them with the salutation: "Dear Ed and Charlotte." The book also inspired a number of long-distance telephone calls, but none I'll remember longer than the one from a woman I'd never met, whose home was some 1,500 miles from Snoqualmie.

It came person-to-person and in the middle of the day. After I had assured the operator that I was, in truth, the writer named Charlotte Paul, a woman's voice broke out, "You've got to tell me what to do!"

Hurriedly, as if she were trying to recite everything she must say before she began to cry, she explained that six months earlier she and her husband had purchased a small weekly newspaper and both of them had been working around the clock ever since. They were green, they were broke, but nothing had whipped them—until today.

They had one child, a seven-year-old boy, and just a few minutes before she put in this call to Snoqualmie he had burst into angry tears and cried, "You're a bad mother! You don't stay home with me the way other mothers do."

Was there one answer, one single but complete truth, to be found in my own experience as a mother and co-partner in a family enterprise? It didn't come to me. I joked about affluent owners of weekly newspapers who don't wait for six o'clock and the reduced telephone rates. I offered the balsamic but utterly false idea that her son was "just tired" and didn't mean it. But I was soothing her, not answering her.

When we were about to hang up, I assured her, "If you're a bad mother, so am I." Such cheery self-confidence, I thought as I replaced the receiver. Well, am I?

Hi and John were in the living room, sorting the numbered sheets of a business form, a typical "at home" job for all of us. I asked them if they had followed the conversation.

"It sounded like some lady was awfully upset," John replied. "Something her little boy said."

"She talked a lot longer than three minutes," Hi observed. "I kept track."

I had been so sure of the truth of everything I said to the troubled mother 1,500 miles away. "Of course you're not a bad mother . . . Mother love is qualitative, not quantitative. Loving your boy is not a matter of staying with him every minute of the day. . . . You are right in working at the shop with your husband. . . . My sons don't resent my working nor do they expect me to stay home with them. . . ." Suddenly I wondered. I had claimed to know what my sons felt. Was I fooling myself?

I sat down across from the boys. "Yes, the woman was very much upset, and she did talk a long time. I thought I could shorten the call if I promised to write her a letter, and you probably heard me say that I would. Before I do, I'd like to tell you everything she told me, and then I'd like your honest opinions about what she ought to do. What you two say is what I'll write to her."

They both nodded soberly. When I had finished a review of the conversation, their expressions were both indignant and disbelieving.

"Why, that little brat!" Johnny exclaimed. "She ought to warm his seat!"

And Hi said, "What I don't get is, how come he's at home? Why isn't he down at the shop with his mother and dad?"

"Perhaps they consider him too young to work in a print shop."

"Huh!" said twelve-year-old John. "He's seven, isn't he?"

"You know what I'd say to him?" Hi asked. "I'd say, 'Look, kid, if you get to work and help, maybe you'll have steak sometimes. If you don't help, you'll be lucky to get hamburger.'"

As they talked, I took notes, which I transcribed faithfully in my letter to the parents of the unhappy seven-year-old. The word "brat" worried me, but after a second's hesitation I decided my report should not be expurgated.

To my sons' advice I added only one comment of my own: "As you see, my boys blame your son for not carrying his share of the burden and for 'being selfish' in a way that makes your share even heavier. But I am wondering —have you given him a chance to do his part? Have you ever made him feel something more is expected of him than staying home and playing with his toys? If you yourself believe that a mother should provide more and more ways for her children to play, and that work, if it is to be introduced at all, should be presented as a 'game' or something to be done 'for fun'; if you yourself believe you should stay at home with your son instead of working beside your husband; if your idea of being a 'good mother' is to shield your son, at all costs, from the experience of being broke or working hard; then it seems to me that in calling you a 'bad mother,' your boy is only reciting what you yourself have taught him, and that's a pity, because if you let him, he might be glad to grow up."

Such a letter was strong stuff for the devoted mother of an only child, and I mailed it with the conviction that she might retaliate with a second long-distance telephone, twice as long as the first and with charges reversed. Instead I received a warm letter of thanks, and a copy of their newspaper.

On the front page, in the father's editorial column, was a paragraph about seven-year-old Tommy. Tommy, the item stated, had just joined the staff. He had a small desk next to the publisher's, and for backshop work he had his own small printer's apron and his own printer's rule. His work was to be limited because of certain other obligations, namely, attendance at the second grade and at pee-wee baseball league practice, but he would have certain specific jobs to do at the newspaper office and in recognition of this, his name would hereafter appear on the masthead. . . .

I had thought about Tommy and his parents many times, especially when my own boys had to be drafted for more than their usual stint at the shop. Two crises arose periodically and forced the *Record's* publisher to call out his sturdy little band of reserves. One was a particularly large printing order, the other was the departure of some member of the staff, usually that most unpredictable of all men in the trade, the Linotype operator.

Within the family, we operated something like a metropolitan fire-alarm system. If the help shortage was merely serious, that constituted a one-alarm fire and Ed took up the slack himself. If the shortage was so critical it seemed two to one the *Record* would come out late, that was a two-alarm and I left my writing office at home and worked full time at the shop. But if the backshop staff was all but decimated, that was a three-alarm, and Hi and John rushed from grade school to the print shop like two small suburban fire companies racing in to save the heart of the city.

Weeks before the Open House party in honor of National Newspaper Week, the sixth sense developed over years as a country publisher's wife had warned me that our ace compositor, Ray Darrow, would leave us before long, probably without bothering to mention it ahead of time.

"Oh no, not Ray," Ed insisted. "He's permanent."

"What makes you so sure of that?"

Ed looked like an old-fashioned cook who has been asked to give a family recipe in terms of exact cups and tablespoonfuls. "Well, he joined the lodge."

"Hrmph. You don't suppose that's because they have one of the few bars in town, do you?"

Ed added brightly, "Besides, he's writing a book about the Pacific Northwest. In fact, he just bought a typewriter from us in order to work on it."

"Bought?" I hadn't seen the record of such a transaction.

Ed looked embarrassed. "Well, we're taking it out of his pay, a few dollars a week."

"He also bought a new car. A great big one. And he keeps talking about how wonderful it is in Chicago around Christmas time."

"He says he likes it *here*," Ed repeated stubbornly. "Ray is not like the others."

"The others" included a printer who had walked out with two small but high-priced printing gadgets in his pocket, another printer who gave us eight hours' notice before leaving to go into business with a salesman whom he had met in our shop, a third man who had been gone for two weeks, we knew not where, before we discovered that during his last week on the job he had made nine telephone calls to West Virginia at our expense.

The gloomy Monday morning in October when Ray

did not report for work, Ed telephoned Ray's hotel. Yes, he had checked out.

"Well, fellows, we're one man short," Ed announced at the supper table. "Ray's gone."

A muted groan escaped from Johnny's mouth. Ray's disappearance automatically elevated Ed from publisher to Linotype operator. It was also a signal for calling out the reserves—our sons, Hi and John. Hi remained silent; he appeared to be waiting tensely for his father's next statement. We all knew what it would be. Until a new Linotype operator was hired, both boys would go directly to the shop after school.

Hi's boyish face reflected indecision. To keep still and wait, or to speak up now. His features seemed to harden as he made up his mind. "Dad, I better tell you this right off. You did figure John and I would work at the shop after school, didn't you?"

"Why, yes. Yes, sure. The way you have before. I'll have to set type, and that throws more work on the other men. You two can take the pressure off by working a couple of hours every afternoon."

"I'm sorry, Dad, but I can't."

Ed looked speechlessly at his older son. He was surprised, a little annoyed, but most of all, curious. "You can't?"

"I found a job. Delivering the *Seattle Times* every afternoon. I have to go uptown the minute school's out to get my papers off the truck and I won't finish the route until 5:00 or 5:30 or maybe six o'clock."

Ed said slowly, "I had no idea you wanted to be a paper boy."

"I won't be a paper boy, Dad. I'm going to be an independent dealer. I buy the newspapers from the *Times'* rural delivery department. That is, I charge them and pay for them at the end of the month. I have to keep the records and collect from my customers. So I'll be in business for myself."

Ed smiled ruefully. "We're already in business for ourselves. The Falls Printing Company."

"I *know* that, Dad. You always keep telling us that. But that's really yours. This job is *mine!*"

Angrily Ed retorted, "It's a very small job compared with the business we are trying to run as a family."

Hi's voice broke. "Maybe it *is* small. But I got it myself. It's my own."

For a few minutes I forestalled the inevitable argument by asking Hi for details. He had used part of his savings to buy new tires for his heavy-duty American bicycle and to purchase from the *Times* the canvas bags in which he would haul the papers. His route, inherited from a classmate, ran through the outskirts of town; he would have to pedal about five miles a day over gravel and dirt roads in order to reach fifty-one subscribers. Monday through Saturday this could be accomplished between 4:00 and 6:00 P.M., but on Sundays Hi would have to leave home about 3:30 A.M. in order to bicycle the mile and a half to town where the truck from Seattle dropped off the papers at 4:00 A.M. The Sunday edition was so heavy that he couldn't carry all the papers in one load, so that day his route would call for eight or nine miles of pedaling, rather than five. . . .

As he explained he watched his father hopefully. Ed was frowning, but he listened without interrupting. I sat between them, my feelings battling each other so fiercely that I missed much of what Hi was saying.

My strongest feeling about my thirteen-year-old son was pride. He knew that over the winter months he would be covering his route in cold, wind-driven rain and sometimes in snow, and at least half the five-mile course would be made after dark. He liked to sleep late on Sunday morning, but hereafter he would have to throw back the warm covers, leave the warm house, and pedal along a country road where every dwelling he passed would be as dark as the winter night. Hi admitted that the friend who relinquished the job had "got disgusted" because the work was so hard and the pay so little. Worst of all, his friend said, was collecting, for even "rich ladies" said, "Come back some other time," and said it again and again. No matter how little Hi would be able to collect for papers he had already delivered, the rural circulation department of the big Seattle newspaper had to be paid on time. This responsibility did not frighten him. For all the hard work, for long hours outside in bad weather, for every tedious or demanding aspect of this far-from-lucrative job, there was one compensation: he would be an independent dealer.

Why, I asked myself, why must we be angry or disapproving? Doesn't this boy have a right to a "job of his own?" As his mother, haven't I the right to be proud?

At the same time, I felt my husband's bafflement and anger so deeply that I ached with it. Ed had never been demanding. A hundred times a baseball game or a bowling match had kept Hi and John from working when he needed them, but he had released them gladly and never told them what I knew—that he did the jobs set aside for them. The core of his life was this business we owned as a family. His personal accomplishments had awakened admiration in some very hard and world-weary hearts, but they meant nothing to him as compared with his pride at what our "junior partners" could do.

I remembered the look on his face one Saturday afternoon when the four of us were working in the backshop. I was straightening up the bound files and back issues of the *Record*. Hi and John had formed a two-man assembly line at the stitcher and were singing a boisterous Y.M.C.A. ditty as they passed little booklets from hand to hand.

Ed was at the paper cutter, preparing stock for a new job, and when the boys reached the second verse he joined them, drowning them both out.

All at once I realized that the boys had come to the chorus and were singing it alone. I looked up to see where Ed might be. He hadn't left. He was standing at the paper cutter, hands resting idly on the heavy cast-iron bar, and he was looking at the boys. Just looking at them, but with such an expression of unmixed, simple happiness that his face glowed right through a twenty-four-hour stubble of beard. Slowly his head moved and he looked toward me, and from way across the shop, the littered, machinery-filled, oily, inky-smelling shop, I could feel *his* feeling and recognize that at no time in our lives together had he reached such a peak of joy. We were all here, together. I knew without testing him that for the moment he couldn't have spoken if he'd tried.

It had been perfect, that brief, wonderful moment, but could it be repeated again and again, as Ed would like it to be? I doubted it. The pattern was his, not theirs. All the things he wanted them to be—self-reliant, productive, thoughtful, curious, independent—these were the very qualities which were now destroying the family pattern he cherished. "Learn, Do," he had exhorted them for ten years or more, not seeing, or perhaps not wanting to see, that eventually he could not tell them what it was worth-while to learn and to do.

And so, with Hi on the one side and Ed on the other, I was torn in two, and retreated behind the cowardly wish that the issue had never come up. Groping for a compromise, I said, "Hi, couldn't you wait until we find a Linotype operator, and then take over the route?"

"Who knows when that's going to be? The boy I'm getting the route from wants to quit. If I don't take it, the man from the *Times* will find someone else."

"We might locate a new operator right away."

Hi retorted grimly, "And you might not find one for two or three months."

Ed threw his napkin down. "We've got a real problem. From now until Christmas is the busiest time of year, the period when we have to make it or we won't be able to squeak through the slack months after New Year's. We could use more help than we had even when Ray was with us. Without Ray, we're in a jam. Dammit, I counted on you. Now, right now, is when I need you."

"I'll work Saturdays until three."

"That's the time you have to start delivering the *Times?*"

"Yes. And I could work Sundays."

"After you've finished delivering the *Times?*"

"Yes."

With an angry gesture Ed pushed his plate away from him. "If Ray Darrow hadn't skipped out on us I wouldn't object. But why the devil did you pick this particular time to go out and get a job?"

If *we* hadn't known Ray Darrow was going to leave, how could Hi have known. . . ? I was about to make things much worse by telling my husband he wasn't being logical when I realized that something remarkable had taken place. Angry as he was that the boy had taken this step without consulting us, confused as he was because our junior partner seemed to be failing us, he hadn't forbidden Hi to take the job and even as he was exploding, "Why the devil . . ." he was moving toward acceptance of the job as a fait accompli.

Ed stood up. "I just want you to understand one thing, young man. You got this job on your own, and you're going to run it on your own. There are going to be some cold, miserable Sunday mornings when you have to get up at 3:30 and bike ten miles, but don't you come to me and ask if I'll take you around in the car. And don't expect your mother to wake you up, either, or make a lunch for you. You've got an alarm clock. Set it. If you want to take a sandwich with you, make it. When you get ready, and when you leave, do it quietly. I won't have you waking up everyone in the house."

Hi stood up, too. He was shorter than Ed, and his attempt to look just as stubborn and manly as his father was not completely successful for his shoulders were narrow and his mouth was soft and his thirteen-year-old voice hit a soprano note as he replied, "I never meant to ask you, Dad. I don't want any help."

"Good."

"And I'll work at the shop on Saturdays and Sundays."

Ed replied stiffly, "I'd appreciate it."

Thus an angry father compromised with a rebellious son, but the invisible tug of war continued. It had grown beyond a simple challenge between generations; all four of us were involved. In a sense, I envied the boys, for their parts were clear-cut. Hi wanted to be on his own and was willing to fight for it. Johnny was almost ready to be on his own and prudently chose to support Hi, as a kind of prepaid insurance against the day of his own rebellion. Ed and I were burdened with less acceptable emotions which, in the smoke of battle, we couldn't even identify. I had a clear eye for proof that whatever he said, Ed resented Hi's independence, and Ed had no difficulty identifying the smallest sign of Momism in me. But he denied the resentment and I was infuriated by the suggestion that I might be an overprotective mother. Worst of all, the natural struggle between parents and children had caused such erosion that now, in an indefinable way, there was something wrong between the two of us.

There were benefits from Hi's paper route which we hadn't anticipated. Protecting his right to keep this job "of his own," Hi worked at our family enterprise with more spirit and energy than he had shown for many months. Knowing the parental boom would be lowered if his school work appeared to suffer at the hands of the paper route, he began to give the teacher the kind of attention she had been demanding futilely ever since the opening of school; as a result, his grades actually improved. Most important, he made his first unsteady steps toward the wise and efficient use of time. With papers to deliver, accounts to keep, and bills to collect, plus his obligation to prove to his father that he could do as much for the Falls Printing Company on Saturday and Sunday as he had ever done weekdays after school, our thirteen-year-old son had a great many things to do and they all had to be done well. So in a youthful, somewhat erratic way, he began to plan, to concentrate, to evaluate.

He even cleaned up his room. The little boy who hadn't been able to part with anything suddenly threw away all the space-consuming mementos I had been eyeing daringly with the thought of removing them stealthily while he was at school. Circus posters, faded felt pennants, pictures of dogs, ships and baseball pros, were stripped from the walls. Comic books, ticket stubs and four collections—stamps, rocks, foreign coins and matchbooks—were swept from the desk, revealing, for the first time in years, that it really had a very spacious surface.

Johnny retrieved two-thirds of this wonderful trash and nested it lovingly in the nooks and crannies of his own room, which was considerably smaller than Hi's. The rest was burned, and then, in the monastic simplicity and cleanliness of his now almost empty bedroom, Hi set up the office of an independent dealer for the rural division of the *Seattle Times*: his "serves," a notebook containing an exact daily record of all deliveries, one loose-leaf sheet to each subscriber; next to that, in martial line, a row of pencils and pens; a file folder in which he kept his insurance policy and several other important documents. And finally, the only decoration he allowed to be tacked onto the pristine surface of the wall, a large page of illustrations of the various premiums he could win by getting new subscriptions.

"The dream sheet," Ed grumbled when he saw this last item. "Forty years ago I was selling subscriptions to *Grit* magazine, running my legs off to get a cheap flashlight or a pocketknife."

Hi said defensively, "Those premiums aren't cheap. I saw a baseball mitt one of the other kids got. It was a good mitt."

"You could do a lot better selling subscriptions to the *Snoqualmie Valley Record*. I'll give you a one-dollar commission for every new one, fifty cents for a renewal. Cash."

"I don't think I should, Dad. I mean, I don't think the *Times* would like it."

"You did when you were eight years old!" Ed broke out furiously. "You walked miles, way out into the country. Several times you were gone all day. But you earned your own way to Y.M.C.A. camp and I've never been prouder of you."

"I'm sorry, Dad, but I'm sure the *Times* wouldn't want one of its dealers to be selling another paper."

"Will you ask Mr. What's His Name, the one who comes out every day on the truck?"

Almost tearfully, Hi replied, "No, Dad, I won't."

Without a word, Ed walked out of the room.

I called after him, "Smoky, wait . . ." but the old nickname, so little used in the last few months, came out as little more than a hoarse whisper. "Dad," I said more firmly, and this time he heard and turned around. "Don't be impatient."

Unsmiling, he retorted, "I am showing more patience with that boy than he deserves, and certainly twice as much as you have for me."

I felt as if my appeal had been snatched away and used

as a weapon against me. "That's unfair," I said weakly. "I want to work with you, not against you."

"All right, Mom," he said quietly. "Then please don't interfere."

The next day was Sunday, Hi's first on the job. All Saturday evening I waited tensely for signs that he had remembered and was abiding by his father's instructions. If you want a lunch, make it yourself. If you have to get up at 3:30, set your own alarm. . . . The click of the refrigerator door, the clatter of the breadbox as it was opened, would have been the most soothing sounds in the world, but I didn't hear them, and since Hi was in his room there was no way of reassuring myself about the alarm clock without openly asking him if he'd set it.

As Hi's mother, I longed to make sandwiches for him, to remind him to lay out warm clothes, and to check about the clock. But to Ed's wife, such prompting was a breach of faith. Caught between a mother's concern and a wife's loyalty, I thought of numerous devices by which I could help Hi without appearing to hover over him. For example, there would be nothing underhanded about asking, in Ed's presence, "Oh, by the way, Hi, did you find the bowl of tuna fish when you were making your sandwiches?" Or when both boys were in the room I might say jokingly to Johnny, "Don't *you* get up, old man, if you hear Hi's alarm. . . ." But my conscience would have no part of such devious methods so the two of us spent a long and miserable evening together. I escaped my arbitrary sidekick long enough to push the bananas into a spot on the kitchen table where Hi would have to see them even if his eyes were half closed. Then I took two aspirin tablets and half a sleeping pill, and went to bed.

Our house is a sprawling open-L with the boys' bedrooms and bath at one end and our quarters at the other; approximately 2,000 square feet of long, narrow living space separates the two areas. When I woke up in what appeared to be the middle of the night, I lay very still, thinking some sharp sound must have disturbed me. But the silence was as thick and all-pervading as the darkness. Carefully, so as not to disturb Ed, I turned the face of the bedside clock toward me. It was 3:15 A.M. Hi. . .

Had I heard him getting up, at the other end of the house? It was unlikely, if not impossible. Still as a corpse, tense with the effort to hear, I lay in bed and waited and listened.

In a few minutes I heard the gentle closing of a door, and a moment later, very faintly, the characteristic rustling of new blue jeans when a boy is walking and one pant-leg rubs against the other. Suddenly I was aware of another sound, or rather the lack of it: Ed's heavy breathing had stopped. He was lying as still as I, and he was just as tensely wide-awake.

Without acknowledging our mutual night watch, we listened, identifying each echoed sound, mentally following our son's progress from bedroom to kitchen to the backyard where his bicycle was parked. He tiptoed past our window, pushing his bike through the grass at the side of the gravel driveway rather than riding it noisily down the center.

Not until then did either of us speak. Ed sprang out of bed, went to the window, and pulled back the drape. "It's beginning to rain."

"I was afraid it might."

"The wind's coming up. Damn these winds of ours."

"Yes."

"It's a lot colder than it was last night."

"The weatherman predicted a low of thirty-five. Not quite freezing."

He stood at the window for a long time, looking into

the cold, black, windy night, until I said, "Get back into bed. You'll catch cold."

"I'd better take him around in the car."

"No, you shouldn't. You told him not to expect help from you and he hasn't asked for it."

"On a night like this, I'd like to give him a lift."

"Of course you would," I replied, and each word tasted bitter. "I would have liked to make him a lunch."

So Ed went back to his bed. But he didn't sleep well, and neither did I. My hip seemed to ache more than ever, and each time I awakened and turned, seeking a comfortable position, I was aware that Ed was as restless as I. At half past seven, Hi's bicycle rolled past the bedroom window and into the yard. Ed and I were sound asleep before he had parked it and let himself into the house.

3

DURING THE LONG HOURS of typesetting which Ray Darrow's disappearance dropped into the lap of the *Record's* publisher, Ed was sustained by two emotions. One was a sense of emergency, such as the owners of milk processing plants feel when the pipes start to freeze, and the other was hope. He had to get the paper out, but surely tomorrow's clean bright dawn would bring with it a competent, sober Linotype operator.

The man who finally arrived to save the day would never have passed for a Godsend if Ed hadn't been sitting at that fearful machine for two shifts a day. His name was Bart Luther. He stood six feet three in his socks, which were visible through the soles of his shoes, and he had the chest and arms of a weightlifter and a large head, all but the eyes and ears sprouting wiry red hair. He walked into the shop through the back door, correctly identified the publisher as the man who needed a shave, and looming over Ed asked, "Need an operator?"

Ed's impulse was to shout, "You're hired!" but this method of staffing the shop had got us into trouble once or twice, and he had resolved to be cautious. A particularly difficult job of typesetting was pinned to the machine; Ed had almost run out of reasons for not getting to work on it. "I'll be glad to give you a trial," he said crisply to the reddish, bullish giant.

When Bart sat down he slumped forward until his legs seemed to encircle the machine, uniting his feet on the opposite side, and the exact spot on which he was sitting was a point halfway up his spine. Shoulders dropping forward, chin jutting, his eyes half closed, Bart lifted two great hairy arms and began to set type. Our machine had resisted other operators, but there was something in this man's posture which suggested even an inanimate object had better coöperate or be beaten to death. Ed couldn't have finished the job in an hour. In ten minutes Bart was thrusting a galley proof under Ed's nose and saying, "What else you got?"

"Go up front and give your social security number to the bookkeeper." Ed's sworn promise to be more careful must have flickered across his mind, because he added quickly, "Oh, by the way, where did you work last?"

"Skibo."

Skibo is an isolated logging town where the shoe-store window is full of calked boots, and Saturday night celebrants fight first and arbitrate later, if possible. Skibo has its own newspaper and we had met the editor; we guessed (quite accurately) that when Bart left, his staff had been reduced one hundred percent.

Ed asked, "You worked for Bill Sodermann?"

Bart nodded. "He's going to send me my laundry, soon as I let him know where I'm at."

Until then we hadn't wondered why Bart had neither luggage nor a coat or jacket. He was clothed in work trousers and a cotton flannel shirt with the sleeves rolled up to the elbows; even the rugged men of Skibo wear more than that in November.

"Your suitcase?" I asked.

"Didn't have time to go back for it," he answered matter-of-factly. "Well, I'll go talk to your bookkeeper."

The moment he was out of sight I closed in on my cautious, businesslike husband. "Do you realize what kind of a man you just hired?" I began in a fierce whisper. "Turning over one of the most important jobs in the shop to someone who, someone who . . ."

"Who just got run out of a town like Skibo." Ed sighed. "Did you see how he polished off that job? He's an operator!"

"That's what they found out in Skibo!"

Ed grinned. "Don't be so nervous, honey. He can set type. That means I'll get back to a nice, easy sixty-hour week, and the kids can play baseball on Saturdays, and you'll have time to finish your book."

"That sounds wonderful. But Ed, listen. We've hired a good many characters, but this time at least we know where he comes from. Why don't you telephone Bill Sodermann?"

Ed shrugged. "I don't believe in that business of checking with a previous employer. He'll say one of two things. That the man was a bum so he fired him, or the man was a good operator but he quit so he's a bum."

"At least you could ask why he had to leave town."

"Mm, sure," Ed agreed. "I'd like to know that myself."

The long-distance call to the Skibo *Reporter* lasted twenty minutes, but Ed's part of the conversation was over in two sentences. "Bill?" he asked. "This is Ed Groshell, down in Snoqualmie. Say, we just hired a fellow named Bart Luther, said he . . ."

"He there?"

"Well, yes, he . . ."

"Put him on. I want to talk to him."

We hovered near while Bart talked to our brother-in-the-bond—at our expense. Ed's face looked as if a small taxi meter were recording in the region of his inner ear. Bill Sodermann kept saying he wanted Bart to come back to work for him and Bart kept insisting the publisher should send his laundry. After five dollars' worth of this fruitless dialogue Bart hung up. Wiping his forehead with the back of his massive hand, he asked, "When's payday around here?"

"Friday."

Bart looked troubled. "This is only Thursday afternoon."

Avoiding my glance, Ed dug into his pocket and pulled out a five-dollar bill.

Thanks to the local rooming house, Bart was back at work the next morning. For the first and only time while he was in our employ, he went to his room before he went to a tavern, and the proprietor insisted on advance payment of three dollars. This left Bart two dollars; we soon learned this sum was a kind of last frontier. Even fifty cents beyond it, and Bart would miss a day at the shop.

It became a mathematical problem. He was broke every morning and asked for lunch money and he was broke at five o'clock every afternoon and asked for dinner money.

"Give him one dollar at noon," Ed instructed our bookkeeper, "and two dollars when he's through work in the evening.

"How about payday? He'll have seventy-five dollars coming."

Ed grinned. "Seventy-five dollars' worth of muscatel with beer for a chaser. It's too horrible to think about."

Somehow we maintained the delicate balance. Calculations would have been harder if we'd had to figure on the cost of food, but as far as we knew Bart never bought any. He was basically a beachcomber; he foraged in the orchards for apples, picked the Evergreen and Himalaya blackberries which had dried on the brambles along the fence, and if the other men left any part of their lunches, Bart sensed it without touching the paper sacks.

Hunger did not trouble him, but he had a burdensome thirst. We had a quart of vinegar at the shop because it was useful for several clean-up jobs. Bart's happiest hour came when he spotted it. "What's this here?" he asked, tipped it up and drank deeply before anyone had answered. "Mm, pretty good," he said, wiping his mouth with his hand. By evening the bottle was empty.

"If you want to get rid of your Linotype operator," I suggested to Ed, "just fill that vinegar bottle with type cleaner."

Practical Ed retorted, "Not on your life. That stuff's expensive."

ii

Ed's antagonism to Hi's paper route seemed to diminish. There were no more scenes, with Ed unreasonably angry and Hi unnecessarily stubborn. Ed didn't ask, "Well, son, how did it go today?" but on the other hand when Hi was late for dinner, Ed did not scold him. As the days passed, Hi began to talk freely about his job.

We heard a lot about "serves." Fellow citizens we had once known as the Smiths or the Mitchells or the Davises were now identified as Daily and Sunday, Sunday Only, or Daily and Bulldog (edition). Strangers telephoned, asked for "the *Times* paper boy" and dictated messages if he were not at home.

" 'Neither snow, nor rain . . .' " Ed quoted wryly on a particularly stormy Saturday night. "If that kid catches cold, that's the end of the route for him. Absolutely. No argu ments. I won't have him endanger his health. . . ."

It seemed to be the middle of the night when Ed awakened me by springing noisily out of bed and striding across the room to the windows. "It hasn't let up a bit. In fact, the rain's even heavier and the wind has come up."

I reached for the bedside light. Just three o'clock.

Ed avoided my eyes. "Turn off the light, and go back to sleep," he said as he went out and closed the door. Fifteen minutes later our car left, carrying the two of them on Hi's appointed rounds.

Ed discovered that morning that our thirteen-year-old, who drank milk at home, had insulated himself on a cold Sabbath morn by going direct from home to the truckers' café on the highway, where he drank a mug of strong coffee before he picked up his papers. Some of the truck drivers knew him, and so did the night cook.

"Good boy you've got there, Mr. Groshell," the cook confided. "Nice manners. Nothing fresh about him."

Ed repeated this comment when they got home, and I saw that he was perilously close to being proud of an independent dealer for the *Seattle Times*. Forgotten, at least for the moment, was his earlier statement that he would never, under any circumstances, become involved in Hi's job.

A few days later Hi's bicycle broke down, and Ed drove him around the circuit for the second time.

He came home that evening with a crooked grin on his face and the gleam of suppressed amusement in his eyes. "I've been wondering why the laziest paper boy who ever had Hi's route could finish by five o'clock, but Hi can't make it before 5:30 or six o'clock. Today I found the answer."

The explanation, Ed told me, was two-fold.

First, Hi did not roll the newspapers up tight and pitch

them onto front porches or lawns from a speeding bicycle. Half his deliveries were special orders. Mrs. B's paper had to be carried to the back of the house and deposited on the table to the *left* of the porch door. Mr. T.'s was to be inserted between the front and screen doors. Mrs. A. wanted her paper laid out nice and flat on the coffee table in the living room, and she was only one of several who left their front doors unlocked so that Hi could go right in when no one was at home. Mrs. S. worked until seven, so her copy of the *Seattle Times* was to be placed in the neighbor's newspaper box, which stood in a row of rural letter boxes beside the road and was plainly marked in large black letters: SEATTLE POST-INTELLIGENCER.

Secondly, Hi knew all the small children along the route, and stopped to play with them. He was also acquainted with many of their mothers, and of course had to spend some time conversing with them.

Laughing, Ed said, "I've been introduced to two dozen 'neat little kids.' I've learned the names of seventeen dogs, I also know the domestic problems of several couples I wouldn't know on sight.

"By the way, Hi is terribly worried about the McDougalls. Young Mr. McDougall was building a driveway from the road to their garage, and Wednesday he wasn't working on it and Hi hasn't seen him since and *Mrs.* McDougall—she's very young and pretty, Hi says, but I only saw her from a distance and I didn't have my glasses on —well, now Mrs. McDougall comes to the door to get the paper. . . . Ye gods, I don't know how the kid makes it home by six o'clock. He spends thirty minutes delivering papers and an hour and a half making everyone at home in their own houses."

Hi's bicycle was repaired in the morning, so that Ed wasn't called on again. And even in cold and rain, Hi did not catch cold; it was as if his lungs, throat and sinuses were conspiring to help him keep his job.

"How do you like these muscles, Dad?" Hi asked at bedtime one evening. "Feel this here . . ." and he directed his father's hand to his right calf, "and the other one . . ." and Ed nodded approvingly as he tested the left calf.

"Good flat belly, too," Hi stated proudly, thumping his midriff with both hands. "That's what riding a bicycle will do for you."

No unusual perception was needed to guess my husband's thoughts. Both Hi and Johnny had contracted polio, when Hi was in the second grade and Johnny in the first. Johnny's was the lighter case. After hospitalization and weeks of bed rest and thrice weekly trips to a physical therapist, Hi had recovered except for a slight limp. Gradually this disappeared, but the injured leg had always been weak, and we had repeatedly suggested that Hi strengthen it by riding his bicycle.

"I can't just ride a bike," Hi had protested, "when I don't have any place to go on it," and we had not made the suggestion a command. Now he'd done on his own the very thing he wouldn't do at our request.

The fatty paunch and swaybacked posture of the little boy were gone. His back was straight, his stomach was flat, his shoulders were square.

Ed appraised the boy silently, head to toe.

Responding, Hi lifted his chin and brought his heels together.

After a few moments of thoughtful scrutiny, Ed spoke. "Hi, do you remember which leg was the bad one after polio?"

Hi laughed. "That's the way I really learned to tell left from right. You know, those exercises I had to do three times a day. They didn't hurt the right leg, but they hurt the left one so bad I could hardly stand it. It was the left leg, Dad. Gee whiz, how could I forget!"

Ed patted Hi's strong left thigh and walked into the kitchen, where I heard him clearing his throat and running a glass of water. Polio had brought terror from which our children recovered completely, but at that moment, with my own heart aching with recollection, and my stoical husband hiding in the kitchen, I wondered if parents ever do.

At the end of the month, Hi had his first experience at collecting bills. His month's earnings, he calculated, would pay for repairs and equipment he had had to buy in order to get the job. In terms of time spent, he had averaged twenty-three cents an hour. But even this break-even financial success would be taken from him if his customers did not pay.

He was even later for supper than usual. Collecting could not be done during routine deliveries, for (we learned from Hi) it was a rare subscriber indeed who could find two dollars in less than five minutes, another three or four minutes were absorbed by filling out and signing the receipted bill, and the customer who didn't pay took even longer to narrate her individual version of "come back some other time." Meanwhile someone at the end of the line would be fuming because his paper was late. So Hi didn't begin a round of bill collecting until he'd delivered all his papers, and for three nights he stumbled into the house after eight o'clock.

The third night he dropped into the nearest chair. "Dad, I hate to ask you, but could you lend me a couple of bucks?"

"Sure, but how come?"

Hi shook his head wearily. "It's kind of complicated. I'm done collecting for this month. I mean, I've collected all I can, I guess. The boy I took the route from says there's always five or six who don't pay when they're supposed to, but usually they will sometime during the month if you keep after them. Well, some places I've gone back four times, and they still aren't home or they haven't got the money.

"Tomorrow's the deadline for paying my bill to the *Times*. If I hadn't paid for those bike tires, I'd have enough, but I didn't figure on so many customers not paying me. After a couple or three months I'll have something in the bank to fall back on when I need it, but this being my first month, I don't. That's why I have to ask you. Could you let me have the difference, until I can collect from the people who haven't paid me?"

Ed said grimly, "You mean some people have told you to come back four times and still haven't paid?"

Hi grinned. "There always are, Dad, the boy who used to have the route told me. I'll just have to go back again."

"But four times! For a measly little bill of two dollars!"

"That's nothing. I guess I'm lucky that only one customer skipped out on me."

Ed exploded "Skipped out?"

"I guess so. It's a man who lives in that little house in back of the garage. Today it was empty, and the man at the garage said he moved out this morning, but no one knows where."

"Little house in back of the garage . . ." Ed frowned. "His name Terry Cox?"

"Yes. Do you know him?"

I was about to reply, "*Know* him? We certainly do. He's owed the Falls Printing Company $115 for the past two years. . . ." An angry exclamation from Ed kept me from speaking.

"I know him, all right," Ed roared, "and I know where he's living now. I walked past the place this afternoon while he was moving in. Get your jacket. We're going to go see him."

52

My husband slammed out of the house, red-eyed and ready for battle. Hi followed timorously, receipt book and "serves" clutched tightly in his hand.

The defaulting Mr. Cox now lived in a community some ten miles from our home, but that didn't deter the enraged father of the *Times'* independent dealer. They were back in less than an hour. Terry Cox had not been at home, but Ed trailed him to a nearby tavern. Hi could not enter. A nostalgic scene it must have been, with the boy waiting anxiously on the legal side of the swinging door while his father went inside and shook down one of the customers. They returned triumphant. Ed was laughing boyishly and Hi was looking at him with frank admiration such as boys in their teens seldom express toward their fathers.

They had the two dollars. Nothing whatever was said about the $115, and I didn't ask.

A few evenings later the telephone rang about nine o'clock and a man's voice demanded, "The paper boy live there?"

Hi was in his pajamas, but he hadn't gone to bed, so I called him to the phone. "Yes, sir," we heard him say. "No, sir, that wasn't my understanding, but I'm sorry you didn't get your paper. I'll bring you one right away."

He dressed, got on his bicycle, and rode to town, where he bought a paper in a restaurant for more than he was going to be paid for it and delivered it with an apology. We didn't know until he came home from this three-mile night ride that the man who called to complain had instructed Hi specifically *not* to leave the paper for two weeks.

"He said he got mixed up on the dates," Hi explained.

Ed looked thoughtfully at his son. "The customer is always right, eh? Hi, you're doing a good job."

"Thanks, Dad."

At last, Ed was viewing Hi's job with the sympathetic interest one man in business for himself feels toward a fellow. Until now he had seen it as a crack in the fortress of the family, a divisive thing, which he tolerated only to keep the crack from widening. If he could realize how like himself Hi was, how like his own bold voyage into small business was his son's paper route . . . "Yes," I said happily, "you are handling yourself very well, Hi. Dad's right. You're doing a fine job."

Hi's smile was both wistful and proud. "This is the first time in my life I ever felt important."

The atmosphere in the living room changed instantly. Ed tensed, turned away from Hi and sat down at the old oak table. He picked up a magazine, frowned at the cover, and threw it down. "I'm glad you feel important," he said gruffly, "but I thought—I should say, I used to think, that was the way you felt about the work we did together at the *Record*."

"I still work at the *Record*. Last week end I put in just as many hours as I used to work all week."

"It isn't a matter of hours."

I could have cried out—Oh, Hi, *why* did you have to say that! But if it was true, as true and real as Ed's own feeling about the *Record*? Should Hi be kept from saying it then? "He hasn't lost interest in our business, Ed. Perhaps I've talked to Hi more than you have lately. . . ."

Ed interrupted brusquely. "It isn't something you 'talk' into existence. It's something you prove by doing!"

"Dad, all I said was . . ."

"It's late." Ed picked up the magazine he had only a moment before thrown down in anger. "You should have been in bed an hour ago. The next time some jerk telephones and wants you to ride your bicycle three miles along dark country roads in order to bring him a paper, you let *me* talk to him."

"I won't, Dad. Not if it's a customer of mine."

Ed did not lift his head nor reply. Hi waited, defiant, ready to fight. The old-fashioned wall clock ticked off twenty, thirty, forty seconds, while I looked from the man to the youth and wondered how to appease.

But Hi turned around and went to his room, and Ed kept his eyes on the magazine. The battle had been declared but not fought. "Yes, it is late," I said foolishly. "We've missed the ten o'clock news."

At the breakfast table, they were polite with each other. Even Johnny felt the tension and kept glancing from his brother to his father with wide, troubled eyes. When the boys left to catch the school bus, I realized that I'd been watching them so nervously that I'd let my coffee get cold.

Pouring a fresh cup, I looked at my husband's back. He was sitting so quietly, drinking his coffee as if he were alone. A grown man, with broad shoulders, strong arms; a man with authority, control, in his very posture at the table. Yet he looked lonely, even from the back.

I filled his cup as well as mine, and sat down across from him. "Ed, this is going to be a hard day on the editorial side. I'm going to get dressed right away and go down to the shop with you."

"That isn't necessary."

"There's a lot of writing to be done for a sixteen-page paper."

"Come down this afternoon, as usual."

"No, I'd rather go to work with you."

"No need to," he murmured, but he waited while I dressed, and I sensed that he was grateful.

The road from the shop to our house crossed Hi's paper route at several points. That evening, as Ed and I were driving home, we met Hi.

It had begun to rain. Ed honked the horn. Hi called,

"Hi, Dad!" but I saw that Ed had no intention of stopping.

I had one thought, dictated by a simple instinct: my child was going to get wet.

"Stop the car, Ed," I said urgently.

Hi looked puzzled as he kicked the bike stand into position and walked to the car. "What is it, Mom?"

"It's raining. You'd better put your bike in the back. We'll drive you around the rest of the route."

Hi's eyeglasses had no windshield wipers; he blinked at us myopically through a wash of cold rain. "No thanks. I can finish O.K."

"But Hi, you'll be soaked. Come on, put the bike in."

"No, Mom," he repeated, "no need to. I'm used to this. I can make it alone."

I would have insisted, but Ed put the car in gear, said curtly, "See you later, son," and drove away.

I looked at my husband curiously. "Why did you do that?"

"He got that paper route on his own. He should do it on his own."

"That's the rule you laid down when he first got the job, and he accepted it. But *you've* broken it, in fact you've insisted on breaking it. Not once, but twice."

Looking straight ahead, he replied, "There was reason to."

"There is now! It's going to rain hard. By the time he gets home he'll be wet through to the skin."

Ed put his foot on the brake and brought the car to an abrupt, jarring stop beside the road. Turning toward me, he said, "If I had known why you wanted me to stop the car when we saw Hi, I wouldn't have done it. I know when to help, and when not to. Please let me decide."

"Can't you see how unfair that is? Smoky, can't you *see!* When you decide it's time to help him, that's the right time. When I decide he needs help, I'm interfering."

Ed turned away from me and carefully put the car in

gear. "Now you're trying to create an issue which doesn't exist."

Like a rebellious child I wanted to cry out—It does so! I was ashamed of the feeling and choked it down, but I continued doggedly, "You're the one who worries about his catching cold. You're the one who woke up at three o'clock last Sunday morning and rushed to the window to see what the weather was like."

"Hi is proud of the job he's doing," Ed retorted. "He says it makes him feel important. By God, you and I are going to let him do it."

We drove home in silence, which continued unbroken through a miserable hour before Hi pedaled up the driveway and parked his bicycle.

He stumbled into the kitchen carrying the rain-soaked canvas bags. Water ran in small streams from his sopping stocking cap. His cheeks were chapped by the cold wind. Every garment was dripping. In the few seconds it took him to drape the canvas bags over the washing machine, a pool of muddy rain water collected at his feet.

Ed said gruffly, "Get those wet clothes off right away."

"Sure, Dad."

I moved forward to help strip off the outer garments.

"He can take care of himself!"

But I had begun the motherly action, I could not stop it. "Well, I'll just pull off his coat . . ."

To my amazement, Hi backed away from me. "It's pretty grubby, Mom. I'll get it off all right."

Behind me, Ed's stern voice. "He will take care of himself."

In confusion, I dropped my hands to my sides, but I didn't move.

"Better step back, Mom. I mean, I'm *soaked.*"

Ed's voice, affectionate this time. "Stuff those shoes with wads of newspaper, son."

"O.K., Dad."

"And hang that jacket up over the bathtub."

"Yeh, I'll do that, Dad . . ."

What had I wanted above all else, if it were not this very unity? If cajoling the father and scolding the son had brought them together as I'd prayed they would be, did it matter if such harmony excluded me?

I retreated to the kitchen sink, and picked up the paring knife, and by the time I'd finished peeling potatoes, I didn't want to cry.

iii

Bart Luther brought relief to the *Record's* mechanical department, but it cost us dearly, for Bart was a strain both on the pocketbook and the nerves.

His threatening, apelike posture at the Linotype machine expressed his work habits more accurately than we had guessed; if any part did not function properly, he simply beat on it with his fists. Our bills for parts and machinist repairs began to mount.

At the same time, we grew weary of spoonfeeding his wages like a nurse giving gruel to a colicky baby. Being a teetotaler, Gloria, our paymaster, forgot how very cheap cheap wine can be and thus occasionally misjudged the amount of cash needed to render our compositor unfit for service. Bart had to go. But we had no one to take his place, and for that reason might have kept him on had it not been for a visit from the owner of his rooming house.

The other roomers were complaining. And it wasn't just the roomers. Bart had been debarred by every beer saloon in town because of complaints of the regular clientele. The proprietor of the rooming house concluded solemnly, "A lot of guys are getting impatient."

"What is the matter with him?" Ed asked. "Does he fight?"

"Fight? Hell, no, he *recites!* Poetry and 'The Star-Spangled Banner' and the Declaration of Independence and all kinds of stuff like that. It wouldn't be so bad if he did it quiet, but he don't. At the taverns he waves his arms and beats on the bar and hollers every word. Now that they don't let him inside he buys a gallon and goes to his room. That's worse yet, so far as I'm concerned. Last night I walked in on him when the noise got too bad and there he was, standing in front of the mirror and shouting out the Gettysburg Address at the top of his lungs. I can't have him in my place, he'll give it a bad reputation."

Terminating Bart's employment presented special problems. We couldn't fire him without giving him a pay check; we guessed he wouldn't leave town until he'd spent it. That would mean recitations at the rooming house for another two or three days and in that time some members of his captive audience might get as "impatient" as they had at Skibo.

Don, our foreman, solved the problem. Don's home was in Issaquah, eleven miles from Snoqualmie and the Falls Printing Company. "Give me his pay," Don said. "I'll drive him to Issaquah before I give it to him."

I glanced across the shop at Bart's long arms and big fists. "What if he doesn't want to go to Issaquah?"

Bart was big, but Don was from Montana. Don grinned crookedly. "He won't get his money if he doesn't."

Bart was neither angry nor embarrassed at being fired. Perhaps a full month in one place was an achievement for him, because he acted like a Boy Scout who has just been asked to come forward and receive a merit badge. His parting words were, "My laundry ever gets here from Skibo, just keep it until I let you know where I'm at," and then he followed Don to his car.

"What's he got to be happy about?" I asked as Ed and I watched Bart's departure.

"There are four taverns in Issaquah, and he's never been in any of them. Think of it, a whole new territory . . ."

Once more we were short-handed, and at the busiest time of the year. Hi and John responded to this familiar crisis with the best spirit they had shown in a long time. Neatness had not been one of Bart Luther's good qualities. Far from believing that there is a place for everything and everything in its place, Bart turned the shop upside down in his search for some kind—any kind—of liquid, and he never put things back right-side up. In order to get the mechanical department back to normal, Hi and John spent a long day at particularly grimy chores. Sweeping up metal, washing down ink rollers neglected for days or weeks, and sorting type until the letters must have danced in front of their eyes. It took quantities of solvent and hot, soapy water that Sunday night to reveal the weary boys beneath the sticky surface.

"Thanks a lot, fellas," Ed said when they limped off to bed. And they both answered, "That's O.K., Dad."

The next morning Ed drove the boys to school. They left home with time to spare, but they were tardy nevertheless because Ed noticed when he stopped to let them out that the trusty old Chev speedometer reading was just seven and one-half miles short of 80,000 miles.

"Want to see five zeros come up?" he asked, and since there is some of the little boy in the most independent teen-ager, they agreed jubilantly that they did. "Then get back in and close the door."

Rush jobs waited, school bells rang, while Ed and his sons rode around and around the block. Only after the numbers 80,000.0 had rolled into place, did Ed stop and let the boys get out and go to their classes.

Our memories of Bart Luther were not allowed to wither immediately, however, being nourished first by a bill from the telephone company for a series of long-distance calls he had made trying to locate his laundry. The second reminder came some weeks later.

No agency works harder than the Internal Revenue Department to keep the small businessman from feeling out of things, but in our state the Employment Security runs a very good second. Of course, at the Falls Printing Company there has never been such a thing as unemployment. There was always enough work to go around, sometimes twice. Yet the Washington unemployment people like to keep in touch. Through some sort of extrasensory perception which marks the really efficient government agency, they always seemed to know when we wanted desperately to employ someone and that's when they would write to us.

Since Bart Luther's departure, Ed had been doubling in brass. The long hours were showing in the dark shadows under his eyes and the grim set of his mouth as he hurried from the typewriter to the Linotype to the job press. The one breather he allowed himself was opening the mail. On a cold, rainy morning in November it contained two cheering communications: one from the State of Washington Employment Security Department, and the other from the United States Department of Internal Revenue.

The first was a carbon copy of Bart Luther's application for unemployment compensation. The reason he had given for being jobless: "They fired me because the shop was overstaffed." Ed was asked to corroborate this statement by signing on the line in the lower right-hand corner.

The second envelope contained a letter stating that Ed Groshell could be fined not more than $1,000 or imprisoned for one year, or both, if a report on former employee Fritz Sartovic was not received before the close of business on November 5. The envelope was postmarked November 4.

Fritz Sartovic? If the name hadn't been unusual we

wouldn't have remembered that he had ever been in the shop; he had worked for us two years earlier from 9:00 A.M. on a Thursday until quitting time Friday afternoon. With two days' pay in his hand, he had waved farewell to Snoqualmie and dropped from view.

"I think he was that stocky fellow with a mustache," Ed mused. "Or was he the man from Boise? Fritz Sartovic . . . Mmm . . . Sure, he was the tall blond one who said he couldn't work under fluorescent lights."

Ed picked up Bart Luther's application. "Fired because the shop was overstaffed—why should I sign a lie like that? He's an alcoholic, he's a bum. So in recognition of these achievements the taxpayers of the State of Washington are going to award him thirty dollars a week for twenty-six weeks, or $780."

"The reason he gives is just as true as those on applications you have signed in the past."

"I know that, I know that. But isn't there some point at which you dig your heels in and say, No, damn it, I won't be party to the fraud?"

It was true; in almost every case the person who asked for unemployment compensation had told less than the whole truth when he or she filled out the application. The real bonanza in half-truth was uncovered the week we received two forms for Ed's signature. One had been filed by the man who disappeared with two gallons of wine and the automobile Ed bought for him. "Too much work" was the reason he gave for being jobless. The second application had been filed by his successor, who worked for a week and then confided in our bookkeeper that he had done it only to be eligible for some rocking-chair money. His reason for leaving his job: "Not enough work."

Women had been just as careless with honesty. One resigned when she received an offer "too good to pass up." She explained that newspaper work was new to her and she was finding it difficult, while this other job was in a field she knew well and found relatively easy. Had the good offer fallen through? Not at all. She had already told her new employer that she couldn't come to work for six weeks; after she'd collected a nice share of the dole, she accepted the job he was holding for her.

"You know what the rationalization is," I said. " 'Everybody else is getting theirs, why shouldn't I?' "

Ed picked up Bart Luther's application and reread it, scowling. "I could just ignore this. Not sign it, not send it back."

"They'll put the payments through anyway."

"Yes, I know. Throwing this into the wastebasket would have exactly the same result as signing it and sending it back. Of course if I wanted to be a real rotter, I could refuse to sign and return this application with a letter telling the truth about good old Bart."

"Mind if I play lawyer's daughter for just a minute?"

Ed laughed. "Go ahead, oh Portia."

"See that line there . . . No, there . . . It says the payments will be made to the applicant unless you present a 'disqualifying reason.' "

Ed scanned the fine print. "But there's not a word any place on this form that defines what a 'disqualifying reason' might be."

I nodded. "That's just it. Bart is undoubtedly unemployed, so that part is true. We fired him, that's true, too. So the only objection you can make is to his statement that our shop is overstaffed. You could holler, 'It is *not!*' Do you really think that would start a reform?"

Hi and John took the school bus to Snoqualmie that afternoon and were at work in the backshop when two boys presented themselves at the *Record* office. The boy Tom was stocky, red-headed, and freckled. His friend Bill was taller and apparently a little older. They needed to find work, they explained solemnly, because they wanted to buy bicycles.

Ed conducted the interview in the backshop, where he was wrapping bundles of finished printing for delivery. "You fellows look pretty young," he said. "Maybe in a couple of years we could put you to work."

Tom was obviously the spokesman for the pair. "That's what you told us two years ago. We came in here and you said to come back when we were twelve. Well, I'm only eleven but Bill's twelve and a half, and that comes out to twelve. So here we are."

Ed studied the eager faces. "Most of the work around here is heavy, too heavy even for a high school boy. You boys aren't very big."

"But there's two of us!"

Ed shook his head slowly. "I wish it worked that way, fellows. I'd like to give you a job but there's another reason I can't. I'm not allowed to. The law says you have to be sixteen years old before I can hire you."

"Sixteen! Gee whiz, that's five years from now. How are we supposed to earn money when there's some law like that?"

"It is meant to protect you. There's machinery in this shop. You could get hurt."

Red-headed Tom protested. "I worked mowing lawns with a twenty-one-inch power mower."

"I'm sorry, boys. I'd be breaking the law if I let you empty wastebaskets."

Hi and John were in printers' aprons, busily sorting out type and returning it to the type cabinet. But they had been listening, and as Tom and Bill walked past on their way out, the four boys exchanged meaningful glances. Our sons' faces showed curiosity shaded by embarrassment; Tom and Bill were openly envious. Not a word was said. The boys who were too small and too young for jobs looked silently at the owner's sons who were smaller and younger, and then they proceeded toward the front door and Hi and John went back to work.

Brief as it was, the scene made me uneasy. If we were prohibited by law from hiring boys like Tom and Bill, were we violating the same law by putting our own children to work? We had complied with one law by obtaining permission of the juvenile court, and both boys had applied for and received their social security cards. But was there some other regulation we hadn't considered, one which said, in effect, that children cannot help their parents?

My instinct was partly right—Hi and John had been impressed by young Tom and Bill, but the resulting thoughts had nothing to do with work permits or government regulations. From time to time I saw them consulting each other in whispers, and finally John approached me.

"Mom," he asked me in a half-whisper, "would this be a good time to talk to Dad about something?"

I glanced toward the oversized broom closet which had been designated the publisher's private office, and saw that Ed had just collected the afternoon mail and was preparing to open it. "I suppose so, Johnny. That is . . ."

"It's about me getting a job."

I could not repress a sigh. The battle had been between Ed and our first-born, and since the rainy night when I had tried to help Hi take off his muddy, dripping clothes, father and son had been at peace with each other. Perhaps it was only a truce, but that was better than open conflict and I had persuaded myself that it could continue indefinitely. Now Johnny. Another challenge, another breach in the wall . . .

Ed would be hurt by this new desertion, and in the confusion of feeling which distorted our minds and sharpened our tongues whenever the issue concerned our sons, his pain would undoubtedly be expressed in anger. He would not want to believe that John's idea was really his own. When Hi had disrupted the family foursome by getting a "job of his own," John had continued as a willing junior partner; his amiability had been especially healing to Ed because it seemed to prove that Hi was, indeed, a difficult teen-ager. Now Ed was bound to feel that John's bid for independence was Hi's fault, and in some obscure way I would be to blame, too. I dreaded a new crisis.

"Dad's opening the mail," I whispered to Johnny. "Let's not bother him right now."

Immediately I was ashamed. I had defended Hi's right to "a job of my own." Because Ed was reconciled, at least superficially, to the older boy's bid for freedom, because peace had been restored, was I going to keep that peace by sacrificing the younger boy's right to do what his brother had done?

I had almost convinced myself that Hi's desire to break away from the family enterprise had been peculiarly Hi's, a matter of individual temperament, a clash between personalities which were very much alike. John was a different matter. "If you can't get along with John," we often said, "you can't get along with anyone." Yet here was pliant, coöperative, sweet-dispositioned Johnny, manfully squaring his shoulders as he prepared to face his father.

I stepped aside. "Ed, John wants to speak to you."

Ed looked up from the stack of unopened letters but before he could speak, our younger son blurted out, "Dad, it's about getting a job of my own. Christmas is coming up and I want to earn some money for presents."

On Ed's face I saw surprise, irritation and hurt. "I'm going to pay you, Johnny. You can draw wages today, if you want to."

"That's not it, Dad. I mean I don't want to take money from you to buy presents for you."

Ed said dryly, "It seems to me that I've heard that before. As I explained before, if you didn't do the work, I'd have to get somebody else to do it, and I'd pay him the same amount that I plan to pay you."

Johnny glanced at me, quickly looked back at his father. "That's still just the same—getting money from you that I would use to buy presents for you."

With Hi, Ed would have been angry, and the boy would have responded in the same way. With John he was gentle. But this was only because Johnny was gentle, rather than rebellious. Ed's basic feeling was the same.

He said carefully, "I appreciate your thinking about— about buying Christmas presents. But it means much more to me to have you working with me now than to get a present from you later."

"Those two boys that were just in here, those kids Tom and Bill, they want to work here, and they could do everything I do, Dad."

"You heard me tell them that the law doesn't allow it. But, Johnny, even if it did, this is your shop, this is the place you've worked in since you were four years old. Do you mean to say you'd rather work someplace else?"

In an odd little croaking voice, Johnny replied, "I was hoping I could get a job at a grocery store."

"At a grocery store? You wouldn't make as much as you do right here."

I thought—Ed, Ed, can't you see that it isn't the money, even when the boy started off by saying money was his reason for wanting to get a job. A job of his own—Johnny would be saying just that, if this conversation continued. I interrupted quickly. "Anything good in the mail this afternoon?"

Johnny looked at me wisely. From the moment I'd issued the familiar warning, "Let's not bother Dad right now . . ." he had known what my attitude would be. Don't upset Dad. Keep Hi from arguing with Dad. Explain to Dad why Hi did what he did and why Johnny did what he did. . . .

Ed swung back toward his desk and touched the pile of letters. "I haven't looked through it yet. I don't know."

"Dad wants to look through the afternoon mail," I said much too cheerfully and too quickly. "Johnny, you'd better go back and see if there isn't another job for you this afternoon."

Johnny hesitated, but he was obedient and he had never relished an argument, even in his own behalf. I followed him and when we were some distance from Ed's office, he stopped, turned to me, and whispered, "Mom, if Hi can have a job of his own, why can't I?"

"Sometime," I assured him, "Sometime."

"But, Mom, how long does that mean? It seems that it's always going to be like this. Whenever we work we have to work *here*. We can't go out and get jobs of our own."

"Johnny, this shop is your own. . . ." I stopped. This was the very philosophy against which Hi had rebelled. And now, even to the younger boy—the boy who had napped on cartons of newsprint and built castles of strip metal— the job that was truly "his own" was a job in a grocery store. Or any job at all which he would do for someone else.

"Could we talk about it later?" I pleaded. "It's been a long day."

A whoop of triumph sounded from Ed's office. He appeared in the doorway, and sighting me, began to wave a sheet of paper over his head in gleeful semaphore.

I hurried across the backshop. "Something good in the mail? Big order? Big check?"

His distress at Johnny's request seemed to have been dissipated by the letter in his hand. "Better than that. Linotype operator. Fellow in Oregon saw our ad. Twenty years' experience. Owned his own shop but just sold it.

Sober, reliable, and likes a small town . . ." He threw his
arms around me and hugged me hard.

Saved, I thought wearily. Saved for the time being.
Nothing settled, everything saved.

Ed's desk always looked as if the wastebaskets in the
downtown post office had just been emptied over it, but
over his shoulder I saw that a letter with a California postmark had somehow risen to the surface. "Any other interesting mail?" I asked, trying to remember what that
postmark reminded me of.

"Plenty of window envelopes. A few receipts. Couple
good news items. Oh yes, that fellow from California, fellow named Harvey who came to the Open House in October. He wrote a letter reminding us he's interested in
buying a newspaper."

"Ours?"

"I guess so," Ed answered indifferently. "Why else
would he write to me?" And then he gave me a kiss that
was not at all indifferent, and said, "Stop frowning. This
time we've got hold of a good Linotype operator. We're
back on top. I feel so good I'm going to sign Bart Luther's
application for unemployment compensation."

And that's what he did, whistling gaily as he affixed his
signature. The reason for frowning had been erased by
the letter from Oregon; our help shortage would soon be
corrected. *His* reason for frowning, I reflected. But it
wasn't the unpredictability of Linotype operators which
put the worry lines around my eyes. A wave of frustration
swept over me. *Your* problem is solved, I thought rebelliously. But my problem—no, our problem—remains beyond the pale of free and open discussion. Let us talk
about Lintoype operators. Let us share our views on printing presses and job orders and defaulting subscribers. But
let us close our eyes and seal our mouths on the issue
which is tearing us apart—our children.

"Tonight we'll go out to eat," Ed said happily, breaking into another tune.

I wanted him to be happy, didn't I? It wasn't reasonable, in fact it was crazy, to feel mad all over just because he was enjoying a moment of deep and abundant relief? "Yes, let's," I said quickly, and gave myself two seconds to smooth away the worry lines.

4

THE SOBER, RELIABLE MAN from Oregon needed two weeks
to prepare himself for the move to Snoqualmie, so Ed's
long shifts in the backshop continued. To relieve him, I
moved from my typewriter in the front office to the Linotype. I was no expert compositor but recurrent emer-
gencies had taught me to turn out about half the production we expected from an average operator.

On a clear, sunny Saturday morning Ed and I entered
the silent void of the Falls Printing Company and addressed ourselves to a long day's work. We had given away
our tickets to the University of Washington football game
in Seattle. We had turned our backs on the pheasant
season, a minus tide at the beach, and forest floors dotted
with a bumper crop of our favorite wild mushrooms. The
new man hadn't come yet, and this week's work had to be
finished if next week's was to start on schedule.

The clattery, metallic voice of the Linotype and the
rhythmic chug of the job press Ed was running shielded

us from hearing cheerful sounds from outside. But occasionally we let our machines idle while we poured cups of black coffee, and then we were aware of the great, wide, wonderful world of people who weren't in business for themselves.

About three o'clock Ed walked up behind me, reached over my shoulder and turned off the light which illuminates the Linotype keyboard. Though I was an apprentice operator, at best, I understood the meaning of the gesture; when the boss turns off the light, you're fired.

"You can't fire me," I protested. "I'm not on the payroll."

"You've done enough, Mom. Clean up while I wash down the press. We're going to buy a basset hound."

"A what?" I protested that that was the craziest idea I'd ever heard, that Teddy, our Snoqualmie-type collie, and Real George, our somewhat less than real tomcat, were plenty of pets for me, considering that our home also housed a parakeet, three turtles, a colony of hamsters, and thirty-five potted houseplants.

"You've wanted a basset hound ever since the Seattle dog show three years ago."

That was true. We don't like dog shows but we do like dogs, and so we had wandered into the armory on a Sunday afternoon just to look around, and in due course came upon the basset hounds. They looked up at me with big, sad, bloodshot eyes, and I looked down at them and burst out laughing.

"What *are* they?" I cried by way of endearing myself to the kennel owners.

It was a silly question, Ed pointed out to me later; after all, this wasn't a cat show. While the owner listed the assets to bassets, I patted their knobby heads, "shook hands" with several grotesquely big webbed front feet.

We decided that day that basset hounds are amusing and unusual but not the kind of dog you'd want to own.

Nevertheless for three years I had been clipping and saving photographs of bassets, though I didn't realize Ed knew it.

"We shouldn't buy one," I insisted. "But it is a nice afternoon for a drive. We could go look at them."

So off we went to one of the few breeders of bassets in those days. A couple named Bassett, intrigued by the fact that a hound had their name, all but an extra T, had decided to raise them sight unseen.

En route I repeated the statement that we were "just looking," and Ed agreed with me solemnly. Thus Mr. Bassett's greeting at the kennel came as a surprise. "Oh, hello, Mr. Groshell," he called out. "Come back to pick up that puppy?"

"Well?" I said, very low in the throat. "Don't tell me you reserved one three years ago?"

"Not exactly," Ed replied vaguely. "More like three days ago. Hi and I delivered some printing to a store about a mile from here and we stopped in, just to look."

"I have the impression that you looked pretty hard."

Grinning, Ed pulled some bills out of his pocket. "Here's Hi's twelve dollars, from his savings. He wants part of the puppy."

"If it's a young puppy," I replied, "I know which part we're going to let him buy."

At most kennels, it's a buyer's market, unless there's been a slip-up in the production line. Basset hounds are not suspicious of people, but basset hound breeders are. We studied three puppies, and chose a round, velvet-coated, tricolor, who bounced toward us so enthusiastically that she kept tripping over her ears, but by the time we'd discussed diet, grooming, and most of all, the proper attitude of basset hound owners to basset hounds, we felt like a pair of adoptive parents who have just been grilled by a particularly fussy social worker.

"I don't know if I'm worthy," Ed remarked but we completed the transaction, named her Jo, took her home with us, and full of high resolve, set about making a lady out of a ten-weeks-old pup.

About a week later, Mr. Bassett telephoned long distance. "How are you and Jo getting along?" he asked, implying that it was Jo's opinion which concerned him most.

"I think we'll be very happy," I replied lamely.

"Are you having difficulty housebreaking her?"

"Well, yes," I admitted, glancing ruefully at the living-room rug.

"Does she chew on things?"

"How did you know that?" I exclaimed, my eye resting on various mutilated personal possessions which Jo had left at convenient locations.

"You're not giving her enough attention," he said reproachfully.

"Am I supposed to shower her with love and approval every time she makes a puddle? She'll get the idea that she's *supposed* to ruin the floors!"

His answer was kind but firm. "She needs a sense of security."

So we increased the attention we gave her and decreased the number of swats with a rolled-up newspaper and about the time the living-room rug was due to be burned, security burst upon her in a great white wave, and she became a model dog.

Obedience was another matter. She didn't resent our telling her what to do, and sometimes she did it, if we didn't rush her. For example, when I opened the back door and said, "Come on, Jo, outside," she did go outside. The dog books classify bassets as the slowest of all the hounds, but the word "slow" is woefully inadequate in describing the progress of a basset through a door she doesn't really want to get to the other side of. Jo obeyed, all right, though nations fell and new generations were

74

born in the time it took her to move six feet. But her eyes, fixed on me limpidly, would say, "I'm coming, I'm really coming, can't you *see* that I'm doing what you ask?"

We had been assured a hundred times that bassets love people, but we found that our Jo was more discriminating and that, in fact, she considered herself a pretty good judge of character. She disliked the garbage collector, who weekly carted away a fine collection of lovely things to roll in. On the other hand, she greeted magazine salesmen working their way through college with such happy sounds and eager tail-wagging that the dullest of them guessed I was hiding behind the door.

Her taste in inanimate objects was also unique. Of all the things within her reach, her favorites were the little white porcelain caps which cover the bolts at the base of the toilet, but she thought they looked better in the center of the living room and until I finally threw them away, that's where they usually were when company came, especially company we were meeting for the first time.

"I don't know why it is," I reflected one evening when Jo was giving Ed and me equal time, "All other breeds of dogs I used to admire are beginning to look funny to me."

Her ankles were pronated, her "pronounced occipital protuberance" (as the dog book so grandly states) brought her head to a bony point, her pouter-pigeon chest gave the impression that she had just inhaled deeply and didn't plan to let it out for a long time. But she was setting the standards for dog beauty at our house, and it was no wonder that in my eyes dachshunds looked skinny and a collie's nose too pointed and a terrier's legs too long. Jo had just about finished my indoctrination when I received the cruelest cut of all—someone took her for a beagle. I stopped at a gas station where the not-too-literate attendant stared at the dog seated next to me and asked, "Say, ain't that one of them teagles?"

I drew myself up, quivering with suppressed rage, and

retorted: "This isn't a teagle, it's a tasset hound!" I've never been angrier in my life.

Once the social errors of puppyhood were behind her, we felt it showed lack of confidence to shut her into the kitchen at night so we decided to give her the freedom of the house. At 6:15 the next morning our alarm clock's strident call announced the new day, and a moment later we heard the click of Jo's toenails on the slate floor of the hallway, and then the steady beat of her tail against the bedroom door.

Ed got out of bed and let her in, and furthermore forgot all earlier rulings and allowed her to jump up onto his bed. At that point Jo found her calling. For two or three days she waited for the ring of the alarm before she announced her presence at the door, but after that she got her time sense in order and more often than not we were awakened by the tail-thumping several minutes before the alarm was to have gone off.

"Did I ever thank you for giving me this beautiful dog?" I asked Ed one morning as Jo took possession of the major portion of my bed.

"Yes, but no thanks necessary. She was in payment for a long shift at the Linotype." He rolled over and looked up at me, grinning. "But keep your hands off that machine from now on, you understand?"

5

THE SATURDAY AFTERNOON when Johnny made his first serious bid for a job of his own, a full-scale family crisis seemed inevitable. The timely arrival of the afternoon mail and my anxious, whispered admonition, "Let's talk about it another time . . ." delayed the outbreak of hostilities, but I was sure the temporary peace would be broken over the week end.

Hi had gone to work for someone other than his father and at something other than the printing trade. Johnny had the same desire, muted only by a more compelling desire to please; any further agitated efforts to smooth the issue out of existence would be futile. With Hi as senior consultant, Johnny was sure to watch for the right moment to brace his father again, and then, I thought unhappily, the trouble begins all over again.

But the crisis was forestalled, not by Mother the peace-maker but by Johnny the athlete. When the boys finished their chores at the Falls Printing Company Saturday afternoon Ed stuffed a couple of dollar bills into their shirt pockets and packed them off to the bowling alley for a few games before dinner. There Johnny learned that he was eligible for the junior bowling tournament. His love of sports being of longer standing than his love of independence, the job at a grocery store was forgotten. Throughout one of the most peaceful Sundays I can remember, Johnny talked about high series and average scores and his urgent personal need for daily practice sessions.

Thereafter we received nightly bulletins concerning the tournament. At last, the great day, when registration would take place and the teams were to be organized. Monday, right after school. Promptly at 3:30 P.M. I was to fetch John at the North Bend grade school and ferry him as swiftly as possible to the bowling alley in Snoqualmie, a distance of about four miles.

"Be sure you're there right on time, Mom," he instructed me at intervals all day Saturday and Sunday. "Because then I'll beat the school bus and I'll get to pick out a good ball."

"I'll be there."

"For sure? I mean, you'll be working in your writing house. Can you stop in time to get me at 3:30?"

"Certainly," I promised. "Three-thirty. Right in front of the school."

Writing, like rheumatism, hurts more some days than it does others, and that Monday morning was particularly painful because there were so many problems on my mind other than the novel I was expected to finish before Thanksgiving. All the unresolved issues which had nothing to do with a book of fiction were riding my shoulders as I set out purposefully for the little cedar cottage-workshop in our backyard.

At school Johnny was counting the hours before 3:30,

but at 9:00 A.M. on a cold Monday morning I had a job to do and it was up to me to forget everything else. I carried a mug of black coffee across the yard to my writing house and sipped it slowly while I spread pages of last week's work on the desk in front of me. Chapter fourteen. Think of chapter fourteen, and nothing else.

Forget the pleasant distractions—Johnny and the bowling tournament, Hi's new subscribers, five of them in a week. Forget disturbing memories, such as Johnny's question, "Mom, is it always going to be this way? I mean, whenever we work, we have to work *here*?"

Forget Hi's defiance and Johnny's budding rebellion. Forget Ed's unreasonable opposition to changes which are inevitable and good. Forget my own inner struggle— the instinct to protect and soothe on the one hand, and on the other, the nagging desire to settle everything that divides us. Forget my resentment because Ed makes the "settling" so difficult, forget my fear of what these unacknowledged conflicts might do to his twice-damaged heart. And forget the swarm of little things—the committee meetings, the telephone calls, the bills from the dentist and Hi's saxophone teacher . . . Chapter fourteen. The last half of chapter fourteen. Nothing else.

Mechanically I went through the ritual which was to put the anxious mother and worrying wife to sleep and bring forth the writer, wide-awake, single in purpose, creative. I turned up the electric wall heater, lit the untidy heap of discarded notes and manuscript in the fireplace, sharpened four pencils, emptied the ash trays. In a long draught I finished the bitter coffee and set the cup on the window sill.

Blue-gray clouds moved swiftly across the rocky face of the mountain. The limbs of the stalwart fir outside my window bent before a sharp November wind. But inside this twelve-by-sixteen-foot cottage, which was my sanctum, fire snapped in the little brick fireplace, warm air from the heater blew on my back, and the dead-cold Monday morning was slowly coming alive. Being alone with a typewriter, pursuing the mystic rites—sharpening pencils, emptying ash trays, swallowing a cup of coffee— created a familiar alchemy. Chapter fourteen. I slipped into it, closed the invisible door behind me, and began to write.

The trick of changing roles—from housewife to the woman who writes novels, and back again—was learned from my mother, a Wellesley graduate who believed that college-educated females quite naturally develop careers beyond the traditional duo of marriage and motherhood. None of us—there were three children, all girls—used the word "career." Thinking in capital letters, we said, "Women should Do Something." It was more than a belief, it was an assumption, shared by our father although originally he had expected to send three boys to Yale. To both parents it was inconceivable that after spending four of her most fruitful years and five or six thousand dollars on college, a girl should be told, "Now get married and forget all about it." We got married, but we didn't forget about it. We had been educated in order to Do something. And so one daughter became a photographer, another a concert dancer. And I wrote.

Once in fifteen years I met opposition to my belief that a writing career could be happily combined with marriage and motherhood and it didn't come from my husband or children, but from another working mother.

I was in a Chicago hospital recovering from the Caesarean birth of our first son, Hi. However, the luxury of a week in bed was not to be wasted. I packed for the hospital at 4:00 A.M. and in frantic haste, since my first-born's choice of a birthday didn't coincide with mine or the doctor's, but I didn't forget to include paper, pencils, and the manuscript in work. The first telephone call I made when the fog of anesthesia had lifted enough so that I could see the dial was to a magazine editor, who was surprised, and I hope pleased, by the message, "Hullo, Mr. Shevelson? This is Charlotte Paul. I just had a baby." My second telephone call was to my mother, and eventually I notified other close relatives. By the third day I was able to focus on a typed page and so I spread out paper, pencils and manuscript on the hospital bed and went to work.

I was thus engrossed when a big, pink-cheeked nurse entered the room and boomed cheerily, "Well, how are *we* today?"

I have never sympathized with the nursing profession's passionate addiction to the plural pronoun, when it's so obvious that "we" don't feel the same way at all or one of us wouldn't be flat on her back in bed. But I took off my reading glasses, rested manuscript and pencil on my antiseptic midriff, and responded, "Fine, thank you."

She was holding a clip board and a pencil. "A few questions for the birth records," she explained. "First, your name . . ."

It was a businesslike exchange until she got to the question, "Occupation?" and began to fill in the line before I answered.

I said quickly, "I'm a writer."

She glanced at me curiously, then down at the form. Frowning, she reversed the pencil so as to erase what she had written. Her hand stopped, poised over the penciled word. "I already wrote 'housewife.' "

"That's correct, of course. I am a housewife. But you asked my occupation. I am a writer."

"You are a housewife. So that's what I'll put here. Housewife."

"But that's not the answer to the question!"

Her irritation was modified by years of experience with the doped-up, confused and pain-ridden females who made up the lesser half of the "we." She began to reason with me.

"Do you have an office?"

"Yes, I do."

"Where is it located?"

"In my home."

The crisp façade of her uniform was touching a type-written manuscript. Pencils, a dictionary, pages of scribbled notes, my reading glasses, all but concealed the medicinally pure counterpane. But she said, "You work at home. That's what I mean. You're a housewife."

"I'm a writer!" I protested, as energetically as a full complement of stitches and surgical clamps would permit.

"Mrs. Groshell," she said sternly, "we can't put *that* down," and since I was in no condition to come to grips with her, that's the way the legal record stands.

Sometimes when I described my writing career as "adjustable," I realized the word was an apology to just such persons as that overbearing, too-cheerful nurse. I want to Do something, I must Do something, but I promise that this thing I want and must Do will not detract from my devotion to my husband or my dedication to my children.

In a propitiatory mood, I once asked my sons how they felt about having a mother who was also a writer.

Even at ten years of age, Hi answered questions as if he were an entire debate team. He pointed out that he had only one mother, and that he'd had very little opportunity to observe other people's mothers. At length he concluded that the disadvantages (his socks had holes in them, he was the only student in the eighth grade whose mother contributed store-bought rather than homemade cookies to Parents Club meetings, etc.) were outweighed by this advantage: "You always do a lot of studying when you're writing," he said, "and you talk to us about it. That way we learn a lot of things."

Eight-year-old John had a two-part answer which impressed me so much I asked him to write it down. "It is a good thing to have a mother who writes," he printed on a sheet of lined notebook paper I now treasure, "because of two things. One is, you get to read your own mother's books with no expense, hardly. Two is, it helps pay for different things, sometimes."

A perfect performance as wife-mother-writer could be achieved, I felt, by scheduling. So much time for the newspaper and printing plant. So much for working in my little writing studio behind the house. So much for shopping and gardening and cooking. And so much—so very much, as they grew older—for driving Hi and John from school to the Y.M.C.A. to home to the county fieldhouse to the shop to the dentist's office. It was no wonder that the afternoon our doctor telephoned and asked, "Weren't you going to bring John in for a refraction?" I answered brightly, "No, I think he plays second base."

Every working mother has moments when she feels like the amateur juggler who was getting along fine until someone in the wings tossed in an extra ball. Such a moment for me was the Easter I failed to buy candy eggs for the traditional Sunday morning egg hunt.

In previous years pounds and pounds of pink, yellow and green candy had been hidden "by the Easter bunny" behind curtains, under sofa cushions, between books. On Sunday morning the boys raced around the house, withdrawing the treasure from hiding places they knew by heart and dropping it into paper sacks appropriately monogrammed in crayon. But the year Hi was nine years old and Johnny was seven and a half, I felt they were no longer little boys.

The Easter bunny . . . What a silly business for boys

who three years earlier had instantly identified Santa Claus as the high school football coach. Why perpetuate a custom which contributed nothing to the children except dental cavities? Hushing the voice of doubt, I bought no candy.

I was awakened that Easter morning by the sound of whispering and running footsteps. The scene in the living room was a happy one. John was skidding around the room on stockinged feet, a worn shopping bag in his hand. On it the word "John" had been scrawled in red crayon, surrounded by free-hand artwork following an Easter theme. As John hurried from one preferred hiding place to the next, plucking the candy and dropping it into the big brown sack, Hi followed, smiling ecstatically and exclaiming whenever his brother uncovered a new nest. There was no sack in his own hand.

My heart contracted as I looked more closely at the candy the Easter bunny had left. Not eggs. This year the marvelous hare had laid quantities of chipped red-and-white striped Christmas candy, orange and black jelly beans strikingly like those we'd served at a Halloween party the year before, and some candy corn and gumdrops which looked as if they'd been at the bottom of a canister for a long, long time.

"I should have realized . . ."

Behind John's back, Hi gestured frantically. "Say, Mom, I wanted to show you something in the other room."

In hoarse whispers, he explained what he had done. When I unpacked the box of groceries Saturday afternoon, he saw it contained no candy eggs and guessed that there was to be no Sunday morning hunt.

"So I decided to take care of it," he told me matter-of-factly. "It was hard because you sent us to bed at eight o'clock and then you stayed up for a long time. I got sleepy. I tried to get in an uncomfortable position so I wouldn't go to sleep, but I did, anyway. When I woke up, I was scared it was morning, but it was three o'clock . . ."

For fear of waking John, he had not turned on the lights. In total darkness he explored the kitchen until he came upon the canister with its store of cracked, faded, sticky candy, and in darkness he groped around the house, poking bits of Christmas and Halloween goodies into crevices favored by the Easter bunny.

"I thought you were too old for Easter egg hunts."

"I am. But John's seven and a half."

"Don't you think seven and a half is too old to believe in the Easter bunny?"

"Mom," Hi said patiently, "John doesn't believe the bunny left the candy. But he still likes to hunt for it."

"If I had thought, if I hadn't been so tired . . . Hi, why didn't you speak up yesterday, when you saw I hadn't bought Easter eggs?"

He shrugged. "I don't know, exactly."

He was being evasive, and it surprised and troubled me, for it was unlike him. "Sure you know."

He looked down. "Well, partly I guess I liked the idea of fixing the candy myself."

"And partly what else?"

"You were so—I don't know, I guess you were tired. You acted like you were thinking of something else."

I had been. My writing. My novel.

"You don't have to look so unhappy, Mom. It all worked out O.K."

"Yes, I guess it did."

"Johnny's calling me." The wide smile returned at the sound of his younger brother's summons. Before he opened the bedroom door, he turned and whispered, "John thinks you hid the candy, Mom. Promise you won't tell him I did?"

"I promise . . ."

For several minutes I remained in Hi's room, so shaken by a sense of failure that I couldn't face the rest of the family. There was no comfort in remembering the compliment so often paid me—"My, how do you get so much done!" Women should Do something, I believed that whole-heartedly. And I thought—Writing is the thing that I Do. But so is mothering.

The fire in the hearth burned down, and I did not bother to replenish it, for chapter fourteen was going well. At noon I went into the house, made a pot of tea, and carried it back to the writing studio.

As I drank it and corrected the morning's work, I reminded myself of the date with Johnny. Three-thirty P.M. in front of the school.

About two o'clock I stood up, stretched, looked out at the mountain, and remembered Johnny. A half-hour later I noted that I'd have to leave in thirty minutes.

Chapter fourteen was finished. Exhilaration swept through me. I looked at the clock. It was five minutes to four.

Pulse pounding, I ran from my writing house to the car, jumped in and slammed the door. "Drive carefully," I told myself out loud, for my knees and hands were shaking. The only coherent thought which formed in my mind during the mile-and-a-half drive to the school was that maybe, maybe I could still get Johnny to the bowling alley on time. "Drive carefully," the one voice cautioned me, and the other cried, "Johnny, Johnny, maybe there's still time . . ."

He was standing alone on the sidewalk in front of the school. The last school bus had departed, as well as all the private cars driven by the mothers whose sons wanted to get to the alley in time to pick out their favorite bowling balls. The principal was in his office, counting lunch

money, the janitor had scattered oily sawdust in the hall
and was sweeping it up. . . .

"Johnny, I'm so terribly sorry."

"That's O.K., Mom."

"Get in quickly. Maybe they'll let you sign up even if
you're late."

Obediently he walked around the car and got in beside
me. He did not reproach me, but he could not accept such
a poor offering of hope.

"I was working, and I lost track of time. I had been
looking at the clock, too. And then—I forgot."

He didn't answer. Braking the car, I turned to look at
him. There were tears in his eyes.

"Oh, Johnny . . ."

It must have sounded like a cry of pain, which in truth
it was, for the sight of my twelve-year-old son trying manfully to keep his chin firm and his eyes dry was cruel
punishment. He looked at me curiously. "Mom, you're
not wearing a coat or anything. Aren't you cold?"

"No." It wasn't a deliberate lie. My teeth were chatter-
ing but until that moment I hadn't been aware of feeling
cold.

We drove the rest of the way in silence, dumb with our
private miseries. At the bowling alley I said, "I'll wait
while you go find out. . . ." He nodded, but he moved
slowly, reluctant to confirm the hopelessness of the situation.

I hadn't thought of that unhappy Easter morning for a
long time but now, shivering and ashamed, I called it up
deliberately. That had been four years ago, no, four and
a half years. How many times in four and a half years
had someone exclaimed, "My, you're remarkable, you get
so much done. . . ."

Johnny burst through the front door. "I can still sign
up, they'll take me, they didn't get started on time any-

way, Jimmy Ribary saved a good ball for me, and I got a ride home, geethanksmom!"

It spilled out, a bubbling flow of words capped by a Gee Thanks Mom. At twelve, the misery of one moment is erased by the joy of the next. Gee Thanks Mom.

"I'm so glad, John. Have a good time."

The words were pushed out of my mouth by a repressed sob. I was cold, near to tears, ashamed of myself, and suddenly, very tired.

He hesitated, turned, put his head through the open window. His frank, happy blue eyes were shaded with embarrassment. "Gee, Mom, don't get so shook."

"I would never have forgiven myself . . ."

"My *gosh*, Mom. It wasn't that important. Besides, it turned out O.K."

"It was important! It *is* important! I promised I'd pick you up at 3:30. I don't know how I could have forgotten. I had been looking at the clock all day. . . ."

Johnny reached across the front seat as if he meant to give me a reassuring pat on the shoulder, but he withdrew his hand and thrust it awkwardly into his trouser pocket. "Mom, you don't feel very good, do you?"

"I feel fine."

"Well, maybe you've been worrying about something, then. It seems like, lately . . ."

"I shouldn't get so shook."

At this borrowing of current grade school jargon, Johnny gave me an uncertain smile. "Yes. A lot of times you seem kind of nervous, or something."

A lot of times, I thought, I have reasons. As I did when you told your father you wanted to work in a grocery store, and one part of me said, "Sshh, don't . . ." and the other part said, "Good boy, go ahead. . . ." As I have a dozen times when being a good wife seemed to be so difficult if I was to be a good mother. As I do when it seems as if your father and I are wandering in the dark and every groping effort to find each other only drives us farther apart. Today the reason is my own. A broken promise, a failure as a mother. And such a senseless, incomprehensible failure, too, for a mother whose sons seem to need her so seldom . . .

Stop being emotional, I told myself sharply, stop pushing the burden of your disappointment in yourself onto a twelve-year-old boy who wants nothing more than to go inside and start bowling.

"If you don't get in there, you *will* be too late." I turned the key in the ignition.

"You're sure—I mean, you're really O.K., Mom?"

"Of course I am." I smiled, and his responding smile expressed such a burst of relief that I laughed out loud.

"Geethanksmom . . ." He ran to the door, waved, and disappeared.

"Geethanksmom . . . Shivering with cold, I turned the car around and drove home.

The warm kitchen welcomed me. I made a fresh pot of coffee, put several recordings of folk music on the phonograph, and while the little volcano erupted rhythmically in the percolator and the guitars and soft nasal voices blended in sad and mischievous songs, I covered the kitchen counters with mixing bowls and cookbooks, eggs and sugar and cheese and milk. Hi liked pizza, Johnny favored peach upside-down cake. . . . An hour later I remembered that I was to have delivered the rough draft of chapter fourteen to the typist's. It was written on my schedule. Too late now, I thought as I grated cheese for the pizza, and for some reason, I was glad I'd forgotten.

ii

Hi came home that evening with two new subscriptions, John reported a bowling score that cost his father

$2.15 (a dime for every strike, Ed had offered, a nickel for every spare), the pizza and the peach upside-down cake turned out well as did the other by-products of my outraged domestic instinct. But throughout the cheery evening I harbored a secret soreness.

It was less a sense of guilt than a sense of loss. My loss, not his. This little bit of participation in my son's activities —a remnant no bigger than driving him from the school to the bowling alley—was far more important to me than it was to him. He could give up the bowling tournament more easily than I could give up the very small need for me which driving him to the alley represented.

As for my older son—when had I last been called upon to enter Hi's life, beyond my functions as housekeeper? (When had he even asked me to make pizza?) Ed resented Hi's dedication to the *Times* paper route, but when Hi had had difficulty collecting bills, it was Ed who helped him. When the weather had been so bad Hi accepted a ride, Ed had driven the car. Mine, and welcome to it, was the impersonal chore of washing and ironing the muddy, sodden clothes Hi had worn through the storm, but his father had denied me the personal, direct communication of helping him take them off. What was left for a mother to do? Had there been times when I could have participated, and hadn't? The answer came to me immediately. Yes. The grade school basketball games.

They always took place during the afternoon session, starting at 1:30 or 2:00 P.M. Hi knew that at that hour I was either writing at home or working at the *Record*. He had never asked me to come to a game.

If he had been sorry because I was not among the faithful mothers who waved and cheered (and coached) from the spectators' benches, his loss was smaller than mine in not being there.

"I might go to the game Thursday," I said casually.

Hi exclaimed, "Honest?" Immediately he regretted his boyishness. With a shrug he said, "It might not be much of a game. We're in the cellar, and we're playing the best team in the league."

"No, I really want to come."

"Well . . ." Beneath his studied diffidence was a wistfulness that made me swear no committee meeting, nor work at the newspaper, nor deadline on chapter fifteen would keep me away from that game. If his father could share, occasionally, in something as sacred as his paper route, his mother could wave, cheer and coach at the basketball game.

On Thursday afternoon I joined the six or seven mothers who made up the rooting section for Hi's team. They had all been Den Mothers and thus completed basic training for grade school basketball teams.

The acoustics of the old wooden gymnasium multiplied every sound. Cheers, calls, whistles, bellows and squeals hit the high-beamed ceiling and bounced back to collide with the fresh outbreak of cheers, calls and whistles.

The veterans of Cub dens sat through it smilingly, and so did the grade school teachers, who looked peaceful and pleased, probably because their eardrums had long since been shattered in the line of duty. Only the coaches looked nervous. Their faces were tense as they paced up and down the sidelines like fathers who have been warned to expect a multiple birth.

All players were on the floor—first teams, second teams, and the leftovers. Like grade school boys the country over, all the players seemed to be a bit too tall and thin, or else a bit too heavy for their height, but the members of the "third team"—that is to say, all the boys who were not on the first or second teams—were the skinniest, the most ungainly, the ones with the biggest feet and the boniest knees, or the littlest, roundest boys, with dimples in their elbows, and trunks which came down to their knees. But they were on the floor with the others, each hapless bench-warmer lining up eagerly for a turn at the basket, passing the ball with a fine, confident snap of the wrist. Our Team, *über Alles*, their freckled faces said.

Mingling in the marvelous din was the uncertain bass of boys whose voices were changing, and the strident coloratura of the thirteen-year-old girl who can, as few mature vocalists could hope to do, hit C above High C without displacing her chewing gum. As game time approached, the disorganized noise abated, the second team and the scrubs left the floor and sat down on the benches, and the starting players began patting each other's shoulders in a sportsmanlike, absent-minded way.

At that point three girls wearing white pleated skirts and long-sleeved pullovers bounced onto the floor.

"What do they need cheerleaders for?" I asked the mother sitting next to me. "Everybody was already yelling swell."

The woman looked at me quizzically, for she hadn't heard me. "That one on the end," she shouted, "is my niece."

The cheerleaders were succeeded by the songleaders, three pretty girls in bright, flared jumpers held aloft by three layers of petticoats. At length the whistles blew, and the game began.

In a corner of the gym, suspended from the ceiling like a hornet's nest under a corner eave, was a box housing a time clock. When the game began, the shutters of the time clock booth opened, revealing the smiling faces of two of Hi's classmates. The two boys kept score faithfully, and with reasonable accuracy, though the fourth quarter ended (according to the clock in the corner) with one minute left to go.

But it was a good game, and Hi's team, despite his pessimistic prediction, overtook the powerful leader of the league and won by two points. Hi sat among his classmates on the opposite side of the gym, but whenever I caught his eye he grinned at me, or waved.

I went home that afternoon with a feeling of happiness too big to contain. Writing about the game was a means of expressing it, and besides I hadn't written my column for the *Record* and the deadline was Friday morning. So I went out to my writing studio, and onto two or three sheets of copy paper I poured my impressions of the wonderful and deafening eighth-grade basketball game.

Two or three days after the article appeared in the *Record,* Hi came home at the usual time but walked past me without his usual greeting. I called him back.

"Trouble today?"

He shook his head.

"Did something go wrong at school? Some difficulty along your paper route?"

I could see that by tremendous effort he was keeping all the forbidden attitudes from showing in his face. He didn't look sullen, or fresh, or self-pitying—in fact, his face was blank of any expression at all. But his voice was harder to control, and it choked as he said, "I'd rather not talk about it."

"I think you better talk about it. Especially if it's something that makes you walk past me without saying hello."

He was angry, but he knew children are not allowed to be angry at their parents. He wanted to cry, but crying is shameful in a boy of thirteen. "Mom, why did you have to write that article in the paper?"

For a moment I didn't know what he meant, and I stared at him stupidly.

"About the basketball game!"

The violence of his feeling astonished me. I had enjoyed the game, and enjoyed writing about it. I had confidently expected Hi to be pleased at such full coverage of an event which usually merited ten or twelve lines of type. "What was wrong with it?"

The accusing words spilled out. "The way you wrote about the songleaders and the cheerleaders. Those things you said about chewing gum and how the boys' voices were changing. Especially what you said about the time clock and the kids who were running it. Mom, it isn't *supposed* to keep time exactly! And you made it sound like they weren't even smart enough to get the time right. . . ."

"There is always some exaggeration when you try to write humorously. You're taking it too seriously."

"Everybody in my class is mad about that article!"

"I'm sorry," I said wearily, "but if that's the way they feel, they're being very silly."

Hi's voice cracked. "I just don't see why you had to write it like that. . . ."

The warm communion across the gymnasium floor; the exhilarating sense of sharing, for four quarters of a basketball game; the satisfaction, as I had written the article, of memorializing this rare moment of closeness in a way my son would surely be proud of . . . These feelings were shattered. Had I been blind? Were my son and his classmates intolerant? It didn't matter. I had entered Hi's world but as a writer I had seen it from above, from outside, and with old eyes, not with the eyes of the songleader who had three petticoats, or the timekeeper who was supposed to operate a defective clock, or the scrubbiest little scrub who thought I'd made fun of his "uniform."

"I'm terribly sorry. I wish I hadn't written the article. But I wasn't 'wrong.'"

"The time clock hasn't worked right for three years. . . ."

I turned back to the stove. "Dad ought to be home soon. You'd better get ready for supper."

I said nothing to Ed about my unfortunate article concerning the basketball game, and neither did Hi. But I could not forget Hi's unhappy protest, nor conquer my sense of loss, and after two or three days, I drove to the grade school for a talk with Hi's teacher.

It was about four o'clock. Hi's teacher was alone in the eighth-grade classroom. She was a petite, bright-eyed woman with twenty years' experience and she smiled when I told her why I'd come.

"Yes, the class was disturbed by your article," she said. "However, we discussed it at some length, and they decided not to send a letter."

"A letter?"

Her blue eyes brightened with surprise. "I assumed Hi told you about the letter?"

"No. I wish you would."

She hesitated. "Well, if he didn't . . ."

"Tell me, please."

She was reluctant. It had been entirely up to the students. They raised the issue, they had settled it, and she had functioned only as a moderator. . . .

My article, written lovingly, had so incensed the eighth grade that a full hour of class time had been spent debating what action should be taken. The humorous touches they saw as sarcasm, the figures of speech were plain mistakes. Miserable and mute, Hi sat in his seat and listened while the boys he admired and wanted to be admired by, the girls he hoped would "like" him, cried out against the terrible thing his mother had done.

There was no talk about breaking windows in the *Record* office or letting the air out of the tires on the editor's car. These thirteen- and fourteen-year-olds decided on an orderly protest—a letter to the editor, signed by every member of the class. Or rather, to the editor's wife, for they agreed that it should be addressed to me. Hi was not asked to sign it.

"But I haven't received a letter," I told his teacher.

"No," she said in her firm, soft voice. "I asked them to wait a little."

"The game was exciting, it was fun. I tried to write about it in that spirit."

She nodded. "I tried to explain just that to the class. I told them I thought that such a letter would be unfair, since the *Record* does so much for the school by covering our games, and meetings, special elections, the Christmas and Halloween parties, and all the rest. At the same time, I felt I shouldn't interfere with any decision reached by a vote of the whole class. So I didn't stop them." She smiled. "The next day, they decided against it, themselves."

Perhaps it was my clear mental image of Hi, silent and ashamed while the protest meeting was in session all around him, but suddenly I was trembling. "I had no idea. . . . If I'd realized, I'd never have written . . ."

"I know how you feel. But it's a closed issue. They'll forget it very soon."

"But I never should have—I needn't have . . ."

Her bright eyes became concerned. "Don't you think you're more disturbed about this than you should be?"

"One time, about two years ago, a woman called me long distance because her son had just called her a 'bad mother.' "

The teacher laughed. "My goodness, that term doesn't apply to you!"

"I didn't need to write the article, I could have written about something else . . ."

"Mrs. Groshell," she said kindly, "there's no need to be so upset."

I thought of Johnny, reassuring me in front of the bowling alley. "Don't get so shook, Mom." With an effort I smiled and stood up. We talked for another minute and I said good-by.

"Don't get so shook, Mom. . . ." On the way home, I counted off the worries I must not get shook about. Senseless, unreasoning fears. Vague notions, groundless as fear of the dark. We *are* a happy family, one for all and all for one, working and living together. By the time I drove into the yard, I had recovered from the strange fit of trembling.

I opened the car door, and in stepping out remembered my one real and physical cause for worry. The silly little pain in my hip. Small, unimportant ache nudging me as I got out and put my weight down. I thought ruefully —It's the only worry I've got I can really put my finger on. Smiling at the poor little pun, I went into the house.

iii

Psychologists tell us that we must work off our frustrations in socially acceptable ways. That is, a disturbed child is better off to go on a twenty-mile hike than to sneak over to the school and break windows. The man who is confused, unhappy, thwarted, should join the Y.M.C.A. handball club rather than the boys in the backroom, where he is sure to pop someone in the nose before the evening is over because he doesn't dare to do the same for his boss and/or his wife. That there are more boys than girls on our long lists of juvenile delinquents, more men than women in our jails, suggests to me (but not to those who know anything about it) that the ladies are far more successful at finding emotional outlets which get past the police department and the board of alienists.

One of these is moving furniture. I've never done this myself, but I have friends who frequently surprise their husbands by putting the electric range where the TV used to be, converting the old sewing machine into a planter box, and so forth. Under stress some of them also feel impelled to change the color of all the walls, a harmless release if it can be accomplished before everyone in the family has painter's colic.

Some women heal themselves by buying a great many things they don't need. Hats, for example, or earrings, and I have one friend who has been feeling nervous for so long she now owns approximately three dozen pairs of high-heeled shoes.

The morning after my talk with Hi's teacher, I was in just the blue funk which drives so many women to buying sprees or furniture-moving or to painting the kitchen chartreuse. My clever, dreadful article would soon be forgotten, and even Hi had agreed that I was taking it too seriously.

"Why don't you take it easy tomorrow?" Ed had suggested after several fruitless efforts to cheer me. "We don't need you at the shop. Buy yourself a dress. Take a nap. Go visit someone. You look tired, Mommo."

"I'm not tired. If you don't need me at the shop, fine. I'll work all day on my book."

"Do you *have* to write tomorrow? Couldn't you drop everything, just for a day?"

"I don't have to," I snapped, "I *want* to."

He gave me a long, thoughtful look, closed his mouth firmly, and walked into the other room. I wanted to call after him, "Please come back . . ." and to confess, as a child might cry on her father's shoulder, that I *was* tired, terribly tired, and that's why I couldn't bear to be told that I was. That my hip ached, that my mind was crowded with worries, and worst of all, that the things I felt I could not talk to him about were so absorbing me that I was in danger of forgetting how many problems we had, and might still be able, to share . . .

For an hour that morning I sat at the typewriter, grimly

determined to write six pages of chapter fifteen if I did nothing else all day. This bulldog approach brought forth two pages, but novels are not written by bulldogs, and I crumpled the sheets, threw them into the fireplace, and left the writing house.

In the living room I cast about for something that would lance the mental boil. Thinking of my furniture-moving friends, I picked up a rocking chair, walked across the room, stood there dumbly for about five minutes and then walked back and set the rocker down in the spot it had occupied for five years. This half-hearted attack and quick, cowardly retreat increased my feeling of frustration. Not only was I old, tired and useless, I couldn't even find a new place to put a chair. Other women decorated a room, I just filled it up. Others arranged furniture, I simply brought it in until we ran out of space. I didn't have the imagination to paint old oak tables shocking pink, nor muscles to shift the piano.

Ed had urged me to buy a new dress. The idea had no appeal whatsoever. Same old furniture, same old dresses. Same old hairdo, I reflected as I threw a doleful glance at the mirror. Center part, two waves brushed back from a high forehead, a conservative row of curls at the back. My hair style hadn't been touched in six years. The only change was in color; while my contemporaries had gone from gray to brown, I had gone from brown to gray.

"Don't ever dye your hair," Ed had often exhorted.

"Nobody dyes hair," I corrected him. "You tint it."

"Well, damn it, don't tint it. I like it the way it is."

Hi and John had always joined the male chorus which sang, "We like you the way you are. If you changed your hair, you just wouldn't look like yourself. . . ."

On that cold, blue November morning, nothing in the world appealed to me more strongly than not looking like myself. I had found my socially acceptable outlet. In one joyous bound I reached the telephone and called the beauty shop.

An hour later I was seated at the hairdresser's, pronouncing the fatal words: "This time, let's do something different."

The operator looked at me curiously. It had been three or four years since she had suggested anything as radical as parting my hair on the side instead of the middle, and of course I had rejected the idea vigorously. Like all beauticians of many years' experience, she was a shrewd judge of character, not only of her customers but of their husbands, most of whom she never saw.

"Different?" she echoed. "How different?"

"I don't know," I trilled, "and I don't care. I need a permanent wave. From there on, you're on your own."

For a second she looked as if she might ask to see my driver's license. But the conspiracy was appealing to another woman, for she knew without asking that my husband had no idea what I was up to. She chuckled. "It will be different," she assured me wickedly as she reached for the scissors.

She didn't dye it, but when I viewed the finished product some three hours later I felt sure this one concession to their wishes would not weigh very heavily with my conservative husband and sons. The middle part was gone; in fact, there was no part at all, for the top of my head had sprouted concentric circles of feathery curls. The plain row of pincurls, which had once rested primly at the nape of my neck, had been trimmed to a soft fluff brushed up toward the crown and the conventional waves at the sides of my head had been pulled straight back over the ears. Areas once concealed by hair were bare, while my high forehead, never before violated by as much as a single curl, was entirely hidden by tiers of bangs. Gone the noble brow of the English major with a minor in ancient history. Gone the clear, commanding profile of

No. 5 seat on the Wellesley sophomore crew. The woman I was staring at needed nothing more than a low-cut red satin gown with black fringe and a bustle to feel right at home in the Dawson City opera house in 1899.

The beauty operator exclaimed, "You don't look like yourself at all."

"Who *do* I look like?" I asked nervously. "Or should I say, what, not who?"

Biting her thumbnail, she said, "That's just it, I can't decide."

I had several errands to do on the way home, and I made them last as long as possible. At one shop I bought several things from a clerk I'd known for almost six years. We had always chatted amiably, and so I was puzzled by her distant, impersonal way of talking with me today.

The curious formality didn't crack until I was leaving and she called, "Say, oh excuse me . . . Am I wrong . . . Aren't you Mrs.—uh, aren't you Mrs. . . ."

"Yes," I said stiffly.

"Are you on your way home?"

"Yes."

She grinned. "Well, good luck!" she caroled brightly.

The closer to home, the keener my awareness of the three-man jury made up of my husband and two sons. Only Hi was at home when I arrived.

His usual "Hi, Mom" wavered and came out, "Hi, Mom —*Gee whiz, has Dad seen you?*"

"No."

"Listen, Mom," he said in a confidential, sweetly reasonable tone of voice, "do you have to change out of that nice dress?"

"Yes, of course," I answered testily. "I'm going to cook supper."

"Well, look, put on some real nice housecoat then, will you? I mean, something kind of pretty?"

By that time I had no inclination to argue. I had staged

my revolt, and I did not intend to tear down the flag, but I nearly ran into the bedroom where I selected a cotton dress with a lace-trimmed bodice and full skirt, carefully renewed my lipstick, and even added earrings and a dash of cologne.

My thirteen-year-old son surveyed the result critically. After walking around me twice, he nodded, "I guess that's the best you can do." When he added, "Mom, want to make a little bet?" I walked into the kitchen, pretending not to hear.

The next arrival was John, who leaped off his bike, ran into the house, and stopped dead on his usually unfaltering course to the cookie jar. The wide blue eyes would not have bothered me so much if he'd remembered to close his mouth.

"All right, all right!" I exploded, dropping the paring knife with a clatter. "Say something!"

Hi offered helpfully, "John, she's got a new hairdo."

John said quickly, "I sure like your new hairdo, Mom. It makes you look a lot—younger." Then he continued on his way to the cookie jar. With his back to me, and in a supremely casual tone, he asked, "Dad home yet?"

"No, he's not."

"Oh, I just wondered," Johnny murmured. With a quick exchange of meaningful glances, he and his brother strolled into the next room.

There is no creature more dangerous than the wife preparing to defend an action she is beginning to wish she hadn't taken, and by the time Ed drove in and parked the car, I had reached full combat strength. As he opened the door, I turned and faced him squarely, a dripping carrot in one hand, paring knife in the other, and pulse beating like a Congo war drum.

Ed's workday had begun just twelve and a half hours earlier. He closed the door, leaned against it, and looked at me. His arms were full of papers and proof sheets he would work on after supper. His chin was dark with stubble and a sticky smear of red job ink struck across his cheek like a saber wound. For a full minute he said nothing, absolutely nothing, nor did he move from his resting place against the door.

He was sure to protest that he had liked me just as I was. He was sure to complain that I didn't look like myself. For both these thrusts I had this counterattack: "All right, Ed, but remember, I *could* have had it dyed."

Suddenly his ink-smeared face broke into a wide smile. "Hello there," he said affectionately, "whoever you might be."

I stared at him helplessly. Hi and John, who had apparently been waiting at strategic listening posts, appeared at the kitchen door and said almost in unison, "Do you like it, Dad?"

"If she does, then I do." He dropped his papers on the kitchen table, walked to the sink, gently removed the carrot and the paring knife from my hands and put his arms around me.

In a small voice I recited the line, "Well, I could have had it dyed, too."

"If you do, choose green," he said, patting me lovingly on the top of the curly, Dawson City coiffure. As his arms tightened around me, he whispered, "Boy, I hope my wife doesn't walk in."

At that point the two boys left the room. They thought kissing was silly.

6

ADVERTISING is the lifeblood of newspapers, so I was puzzled when I went into Ed's office one rainy November afternoon to find him frowning rather than smiling at two large ad layouts.

"Why so glum?" I asked. "Your desk is covered all over with prosperity."

"The size of the ads is fine. It's the message that bothers me." He slid the first sheet toward me.

The advertisement had been placed by a corporation which operates a chain of dairies all over the states. It announced that the company had purchased a dairy in the Snoqualmie Valley which, as of November 15th, would take its place among the hundreds of fine modern plants bearing the company name.

Ed flipped the second advertisement across the desk. "This one came in yesterday."

The wording was different, but the content was identical: A second Snoqualmie Valley dairy had been sold to another large corporation.

Ed placed the two sheets side by side. "It bothers me. When we came to the Valley eight years ago, there were three independent, locally owned dairies. They were all operated by families which had lived here for a long time. Father drove the truck, mother kept books and answered the telephone, the kids helped in the barn when they weren't in school. Now two out of three of them are gone."

"They aren't really gone, are they?"

He frowned. "Both big dairy outfits plan to close down the little processing plants here in our Valley. Company trucks will make deliveries out of big processing plants in Seattle. Big business gets bigger as small business disappears."

I said indignantly, "Well, there's one local dairy left and from now on I'm going to buy milk from them."

"Straws in the wind," Ed murmured, picking up the ad layouts. "And I don't like the way they're blowing."

I made my protest by transferring to the one remaining small, independent dairy, and a few days later a spanking new milk truck, with a corporation's name and widely recognized trademark glistening on its sides, drove into the backyard. A young man in handsome company uniform stepped out and knocked on the kitchen door.

He was courteous, friendly, and very good-looking. He was the new route manager, he explained, and he was sorry to learn that he had lost me as a customer. Perhaps the service had not been good, but he could promise that hereafter it would be better. If I'd been dissatisfied with the line of dairy products, I'd be glad to know that from now on the line would be improved one hundred percent. Wouldn't I reconsider?

I replied that for eight years the service *and* the products had been excellent, and if the dairy were still owned and operated by Snoqualmie Valley residents I would still be a customer.

The young man protested, with a smile, that the sale of this little country dairy to the large company he represented would be a tremendous benefit to the community.

I looked at him coldly. "Why?"

"For one thing, our service. The local dairy used to have two trucks. They were both pretty old, they often broke down. I heard that for two weeks last year the owner covered his route with an old pickup."

"He did. And I sympathized with him."

"But we can *guarantee* our service. We've got hundreds of trucks, hundreds of drivers. They don't milk cows, and clean out barns, and bottle the milk. They're trained route men, all they do is drive. Besides, our products are superior to those a little local dairy can put out."

I bristled. "I'm sure you have more products. But better ones? I doubt it. You know better than I that butterfat content is regulated by law. I'll bet your big company doesn't put one bit more cream in the cream or curds in the cottage cheese than a little dairy does."

He backed up a step or two. "A big company like ours makes very important contributions in the field of research. We maintain laboratories, we have staff chemists . . ." He stopped, cleared his throat, and renewed the smile which had almost escaped him during my outburst. "It's progress, Mrs. Groshell."

I said stubbornly, "We own a small business here in the Valley. We trade with people who trade with us. Does your company intend to advertise in our newspapers?"

"Well, no. You see, we sell milk to the grocery stores as well as on home delivery. If we advertise our home delivery service, we'd be competing with the grocery stores and they're big customers."

"I see. How about printing? The little dairy you bought out used to get all their business forms and statements from us."

The young man flushed. "Well, I'm awfully sorry, but my company doesn't buy from—uh—small print shops. A big printing company in Seattle does our work."

And is the owner of the big printing company on the board of directors of the big dairy? I gulped down the question and said dryly, "*Small* print shops and small dairies should stick together. I'm sorry, but I think you're wasting your time with me and I've got to get to work."

"If you change your mind . . ." He handed me a crisp, clean business card.

The name on it was well known to me. I looked into the young man's face and for the first time saw the deep blue eyes and broad forehead of an older man who had been our friend for several years. "I know your father."

"Yes, Dad's still on the old farm. I'd like him to move into the city, but I can't get him to do it."

"Since you seem to be interested in dairying, how is it you didn't take over the family farm?"

He laughed. "Not me. I know how rough it is to make it on your own these days. On my job I work eight hours, I'm through for the day. Dad worked seven days a week and he was worn out by the time he was fifty."

"He never worked a day in his life for anyone but himself. And he always made a good living."

"You couldn't do it now," the young man said, "not on that farm of his. It's too small."

Hard after the announcements concerning the two dairies we received news of much greater concern to us: Agreement had been reached between directors of our local banks and those of a large, statewide banking organization. The Snoqualmie Valley "chain" of eight small banks would soon be sold to a big Seattle banking system.

Headquarters of all Valley banks were located in the two-story red brick building across the street from the Falls Printing Company. From the moment we went into business on that quiet corner in Snoqualmie we had a close relationship with the bank, to say the very least. Sometimes the money they paid us for printing went back to them so fast it might have been attached to a hundred and fifty feet of nylon line which the cashier reeled in as soon as he felt it hit the bottom of our safe. But they did business with us, and we did business with them.

The white-haired chairman of the board was a vigorous, bright-eyed man of seventy. "We thought about this sale for a long time," he told Ed, "and we came to the conclusion that it was the best thing for the whole Valley. We've done very well. But we recognize that the tremendously big system of banks which wants to buy us out can do a lot more for our people than we can. Ed, I'd appreciate it very much if you'd tell folks, through your newspaper, how much better off they're going to be."

"Are you convinced that they will be better off?"

"We wouldn't have agreed to sell if we hadn't been. Now, for one thing . . ."

The first visible changes were to be expected, and only a few die-hard Seattlephobes resented them. Some Snoqualmie Valley residents who worked for the banks were transferred to Seattle, and Seattle bank employees were transferred to branches in the Snoqualmie Valley. The modest signs, which for years had hinted at what was going on inside the bank buildings, were replaced by mammoth, brilliantly lighted insignia of the Seattle chain, plus a smaller sign for the name of the branch.

I complained to Ed. "On that sign, the word *Seattle* is just as big as the word *Snoqualmie*."

"My dear girl, Seattle *is* bigger than Snoqualmie."

I looked out at the familiar street, where at the moment there were as many dogs as automobiles, and replied, "Not in Snoqualmie, it isn't."

He laughed. "Read my editorial. I'm convinced that the

sale of our banks is going to be good for the Valley. Progress, not sentiment."

We soon learned how big a price we were going to pay for progress. Hereafter, we were notified, printing for the Snoqualmie Valley branches of the Seattle bank would be done at the printing plant owned and operated by that bank. "It's a matter of economy," the executive from Seattle explained.

It certainly was. The work we had done for our local banks—ledger sheets, for example, which we had been turning out by the hundreds of thousands—accounted for fourteen percent of our gross income. "Economy?" Yes indeed. The *Record's* publisher had written in all sincerity that the sale of the local banks to a big Seattle bank would bring many benefits, but to him, it meant losing one out of every seven dollars.

Ed picked up the editorial page, crumpled it in one hand and threw it into the wastebasket. "We're hurt by this," he said angrily, "but we're not the only ones. I've been thinking of Bud Kaplan."

Bud Kaplan, his father and his younger brother owned a small paper company in Seattle. We had been introduced to him by the man from whom we purchased the Falls Printing Company and the *Snoqualmie Valley Record*.

"During the war," our predecessor told us, "the big companies wouldn't sell me any paper. Supplies were limited, so they saved everything they had for big outfits—for department stores, for big printing companies, who buy a hundred or maybe five hundred times as much as a little shop in Snoqualmie. But I could buy from the Kaplans. Without them I couldn't have kept the *Record* going. If it hadn't been for them I couldn't have stayed in business. After the war the big paper companies began sending salesmen around again, but I still bought everything I could from Kaplan's."

We, too, became good customers of the Kaplan family, and we had the same cause for loyalty to this small paper company: shabby treatment by a big paper company.

During our first two or three years, paying bills presented problems far graver than those of tracking down elusive Linotype operators or patching up our dispirited printing presses. Despite frequent transfusions from the donor across the street, our bank account seldom covered more than half the bills in the drawer; lucky indeed were those creditors we got to every other month.

At first we bought stock from a paper company which had a warehouse and wholesale sales plants in cities all over the United States as well as in Seattle. We soon found that they were not sensitive to the troubles of a small weekly newspaper. If we had not paid in full by the fifteenth of the month, one of their salesmen was sent to collect the balance in person, and he carried out the assignment in the middle of the front office while two or three of our subscribers looked the other way and tried to keep from smiling.

By apologizing to other, smaller suppliers, we managed to keep our account current for six months, and then, in the seventh month, we received a rush job order which called for paper stock sold exclusively by this large nationwide corporation.

Ed telephoned long distance to place the order.

"Falls Printing, Snoqualmie? Just a moment, sir," the switchboard operator said, and transferred the call to the credit department. For five minutes, and at our expense, a gentleman reminded Ed that we owed his company $65.15, that all bills were payable by the fifteenth of the month, that a man's only as good as his credit and honesty is the best policy and the sweetest words in English prose are these: Dear sir, find check enclosed. . . .

"There are bigger paper companies than *that* paper company," I fumed when Ed told me about the call.

Ed replied, "And smaller ones, thank God."

Fortunately for us, the Kaplan family did not seem to need money as badly as the big company with plants, warehouses and sales forces all over the United States. A check for fifty dollars and a note of explanation was an acceptable stopgap for a remittance of $200. When the really desperate days were behind us, we continued to buy from them, and the more ledger forms we printed for the bank, the more ledger paper we purchased from Kaplan's.

"Here's what I mean . . ." Ed showed me a sheet of paper on which he had written a row of figures. "Out of curiosity, I checked through old bills to see just how much of the stock we've bought from Kaplan has been for printing we've done for the bank." He drew circles around the totals at the bottom of the page. "Last year, we bought $3,800 worth of paper from Kaplan's. Total cost of paper *not* used for bank jobs: $680."

"There goes the pure silk necktie Bud Kaplan sends you every Christmas."

Ed threw me a wan smile. "Since I've just lost my shirt, what would I want with a tie?" He threw the page of figures into the wastebasket on top of the editorial about the benefits of selling small banks to big banks. "What worries me is the chain reaction. The big banks put pressure on the small ones. They sell out. At that point, we lose the bank's printing to a big printing company; the pressure is passed along to us. It doesn't stop there. The big paper companies are putting terrific pressure on the Kaplans. When the Kaplans lose our business, their struggle to remain independent of the big companies is just that much harder. If they were to sell out, one more small outfit would disappear, and a big company would get bigger."

I thought suddenly of Mr. Frank S. Harvey of California. "If you're convinced that small business is doomed, maybe you'd better get in touch with that man who wanted to buy the *Record*."

Ed said grimly, "Not on your life. We've just lost fourteen, maybe fifteen percent of our gross, but I'll tell you one thing—even without the bank business, next year's gross is going to be bigger than this year's."

"How?"

He shook his head. "I don't know. But there *is* more business. I'll have to go out and find it."

Ten years earlier I would have cheered, but now I couldn't see anything but the strained look around his mouth, the anxiety in his eyes, and for all the bravery of his words his voice sounded tired. How could I say to him—"Remember how sick you were . . . Remember you're supposed to relax . . . Remember you're fifty years old . . ."? With a show of diffidence I hoped would fool him, I asked, "You haven't heard anything more from that man in California, have you?"

"What man?" He was a worse actor than I, for his question was even accompanied by a quick glance toward the drawer in which Frank Harvey's letter had been stored since its arrival the month before. "Oh, that one. Why would he write again?"

"Ed, listen. If you're still thinking of the shop as a kind of sacred trust, to be passed from father to sons . . ." I broke off. I had meant to tell him how deep, how constant was my concern about him, but anxiety put a sharp edge on my voice and I sounded sarcastic.

"Not sacred," he retorted. "Just a family business, a certain way of life, trite as that expression is."

"But you know the boys are changing. Hi and his paper route, Johnny and his talk about getting a job in a grocery store . . ."

"Two years ago they were talking about raising chinchillas."

"That was just a whim!" I protested. "Now it's a matter of growing up!"

He stood up and began to walk past me and out of his office.

Jumping out of the rickety swivel chair, I held his arm. "In the beginning, even before we bought this business, we agreed that we'd never demand, or even expect, our children to take it over when they grew up. We discussed it at length. We talked about the way you'd felt, as a boy, when your father wanted you to stay on the ranch in Montana, and go into partnership with him." With every rapidly whispered word, my fingers tightened on his arm. "Have you forgotten?"

His eyes had clouded, as they always did when anything but the most trivial of boyhood memories was evoked. "No, I haven't forgotten," he said bitterly. "I haven't forgotten one damn thing. Including how nice it was when the four of us—Johnny and Hi and I, and even you—used to work here, together."

He pulled away from me and walked into the backshop, and I let him go.

ii

On Monday morning, we discovered that over the week end our luck had proceeded swiftly on the downgrade. Bob, our printer, always as reliable as a station agent's watch, had all but cut his leg off with a chain saw; he would be at home for some time. Don, our indestructible printer-foreman, reported for work but his right hand was swollen to twice its normal size. The raw knuckles were nothing to worry about, Don assured us, but he admitted that the great red bulging area between thumb and wrist was a little sore.

113

"Get in a fight?" Ed asked.

"Well, not exactly," Don said modestly. "I only hit him once."

"What's his head made of? Look at that hand!"

Don flushed. "Well, the thing is, I hit him with my left," and he held out his left hand, which hadn't a mark on it.

It was a strange moment for a harried businessman to start recovering from the blues, but Don's account of the fight accomplished it.

On Saturday night, Don had joined his friends at the neighborhood social center. He was standing at the bar, enjoying a glass of draught beer, when a troublemaker by the name of Joe pushed himself between Don and a friend. Peering beerily into Don's face, he shouted, "I don't like that such and such little rag you work for and you can tell your boss I said so!"

In the language of diplomacy learned in Kalispell, Montana, Don told Joe to shut up.

Joe wanted to go outside and fight.

"Fight for what?" Don asked. "Come on, Joe, relax. I'll buy you a cold one."

Grumbling, Joe accepted the beer. The bartender drew one for each of them, and selected the coins from the small treasury in front of Don.

Don nodded amiably at Joe and was just lifting the glass to his mouth when Joe picked up his own beer and threw it in Don's face. "I said, I don't like what your boss writes in his such and such newspaper! C'mon out n'fight!"

"It wasn't just the insults," Don explained, "it was the waste of a good glass of beer. I couldn't see no sense in going outside. I figured to get in one with my left, and one with my right, and do it there at the bar. I came through with the left and followed it up fast with my

114

right. But my left dropped him. My right smashed into the mahogany."

Ed sent Don to the doctor's office, and Don returned with news that his hand was broken in two places. It was encased in a protective rig like an aluminum lacrosse racket, and despite his enthusiastic demonstration of how this extension of his right arm could be used to lift a form onto a press, it was obvious that we were going to have a one-armed foreman for quite some time. Some of Don's work would fall to Ed, and while Bob's leg was mending, Ed would have to take over his job, too. The prospects for Thanksgiving were not joyous, if we were going to insist on having something to be thankful for.

And yet Ed's spirits lifted. There was a positive quality to his voice when he telephoned and said, "I'm sorry, but I'll have to stay down until eleven or twelve o'clock. You go ahead and eat dinner with the boys."

As I hung up, the thought struck me—He's relieved. An exhausting day at the shop is simpler than the superficial peace at home. Hard work is clear-cut, familiar; it is something he can finish, it produces positive, visible results. At home he has been living under an uneasy truce with Hi, and the untroubled relationship with his younger son lasted as long as the junior bowling tournament. And where am I, his wife, in the shadowing conflict we are pretending doesn't exist?

Whether it was his fault or mine, whether the blame lay with rebellious children or combative parents, the simple fact was that my husband was finding it easier not to come home.

As if to punish me, my memory raced back to the days when he had loped up the back steps each evening shouting, "Hey, Miss Smoke, where are you?" Miss Smoke, who became Mrs. Smoke, who had once been Miss Smoot . . .

The name originated during the twenty-nine days between our discovery that we liked each other better than anyone else we knew, and our wedding in the parlor of an old-fashioned parsonage in Illinois. Why we had time or inclination during this long engagement to discuss the Smoot-Hawley Tariff Act, I cannot say, unless it was the fact that we didn't discuss what we had in common, or how we could live on our income, or how we felt about religion, politics, or the ideal size for a family.

From this bookish lovemaking our pet names evolved. No Honeybun or Loverdoll for us, Ed was Mr. Hawley and I was Miss Smoot. When we were married, we followed the tradition of the changing of a name, but in reverse: Mr. Hawley became Mr. Smoot, for by that time we had decided we preferred him to the other senator. Thus we entered the solemn temple of monogamy bearing the name of an apostle of the Mormon church.

When we bought a little farm, we called it Smoot Acres; the name was printed on all our stationery. Smoot was written in concrete at the base of the outdoor fireplace Ed built and when we bought an Airedale puppy, his name was Smoot, too.

"Call me Charlotte," I once demanded, on impulse.

Ed looked uncomfortable. "Gosh," he said, "I can't. It sounds foolish."

This continued unchanged until the birth of our first child, at which point Ed, ever conservative, began calling me Mrs. Smoot. The second transition was accomplished by the Airedale and a ditch digger by the name of Jack.

Jack was dispatched to our farm by the contractor who was installing a new drainage system. He was a big, black-haired Irishman who sang while he worked and loved dogs. When he reached out to pet Smoot, the fearful terrier forgot to bare his strong white teeth as he did for the rural mail carrier, brush vendors, Bible tract salesmen and others.

"Nice doggy," said Jack, rubbing the head which had sent many a drop-in caller screaming from the premises. "What's his name?"

"Smoot."

"Huh?"

"Smoot. His name is Smoot."

"Nice doggy," said Jack. "Atta boy, Smoke. Good dog, Smoke."

It took Jack about a week to finish his job and by that time Ed was Smoky and I was Mrs. Smoke. Friends who had been puzzled by the Smoots didn't even bother to ask about the Smokes, though they looked at me curiously when I refused a cigarette. Strangers with logical minds sometimes asked for the story behind the nicknames, but after I explained that it began during our courtship when we were discussing the Smoot-Hawley Tariff Act of 1930, I always had the feeling that they weren't really listening.

"Mrs. Smoke, where are you . . ." It had been Ed's evening greeting for years and years. Somehow Smoky and the girl he liked better than anyone else he knew had slipped out of sight, and the quarrelsome woman named Mom was making home a difficult place to come back to.

The current emergency at the shop was real. He *did* have to stay on the job until eleven or twelve o'clock at night. But the emergency was welcome. He knew as well as I that such a release was only temporary. Nothing had been settled. But for a few days, a week, he would be too busy to think of anything but press work, and type-setting, and newswriting, and too tired to be asked to think of anything else.

I made a fresh resolve. I would try harder to ease the tension between Ed and the boys, and I would forget—

and by forgetting dissolve—the conflict between Ed and me. I had meant to, but since the Open House party in October, my efforts had been clumsy. There were excuses, if I wanted them. I had been feeling tired and the small but persistent ache in my hip had distracted me.

The right moment to speak up, the right moment to silence the boys or to sympathize with my husband, perhaps even the moment when Ed and I could face each other honestly and explore our differences, these had slipped past me while I was wearily asking myself what to do. I will do better, I promised myself. I'll call out Mrs. Smoke and silence Mom. I can, and I will, do better.

iii

The forecast was for freezing weather. From some frigid stretch of the North Pacific a low pressure area was rolling toward us, bringing unseasonal storms.

This warning reached us via the ten o'clock news program. Ed had worked late, eaten a warmed-over supper, and had just come out of a warm bath. I turned to him anxiously. "What about the well pump?"

He sat down in front of the fireplace and looked sleepily at the red embers of the alder log. "What *about* the well pump."

"Didn't you hear the weather report? It's going to freeze."

"Can't."

One simple, short word. Can't. As a college graduate, I felt constrained to match my husband's logic, so I said, a little more loudly, "It can, too."

He shook his head.

"The weatherman said freezing!"

Ed settled deeper into his warm flannel robe. "He's been wrong before."

"He's a qualified meteorologist. He has charts and

barometers and a seismograph and all sorts of equipment."

He grinned. "Then you'd think he'd be right once in a while."

"He has a degree from the University of Washington!"

Ed contemplated the beamed ceiling, listening to the clattering rain. "I've got three degrees from two universities."

"Not in weather, you haven't. Look, it's no joke. We've got to put an extension cord out to the well house and keep a bulb burning all night, or our well pump will freeze and tomorrow morning we won't have any water."

"*We've* got to put an extension cord into the well house?"

"All right, will *you* please put a light in the well house."

"I would, if it were necessary," he replied pleasantly. "But it isn't. It isn't going to freeze."

I couldn't blame him for disliking the chore. The first step in the installation would be to find an extension cord; a frustrating half-hour search would undoubtedly yield nothing and we'd end up removing the cord which ran along the wall behind the reed organ to the television set. The organ would have to be moved first, of course, as well as the brass candlestick, the family portrait, and other items resting on top of it.

Running the extension from Johnny's bedroom, through the window, and across the lawn to the well house would be the next step. The outlet directly under the bedroom window had either been overlooked by the electrician when he wired the house, or had been disconnected by the carpenter who followed him to nail up the wall; in any case, it didn't work. However, we could find the step-ladder and plug into the ceiling fixture, after removing a large chandelier decorated with Mickey and Minnie Mouse.

The extra feet thus added onto the distance from an

outlet to the well house was just enough to make the extension cord too short, so an intermediate connection would have to be established. This was done by plugging a floor lamp (from the guest room) into the ceiling, and connecting the extension cord to it, after we'd found one of those little fixtures which converts a round screw socket into a two-pronged outlet. This useful item, being much smaller than an extension cord, was always harder to find, and we might have to borrow the one on the cord behind the phonograph, after moving the phonograph.

The next step would be to open Johnny's bedroom window. Being on the rainy side of the house, the bottom half had been cemented with durable putty and the top half always stuck in damp weather. And finally, Ed would go outside (after changing back into clothes and shoes) and catch the cord as I pushed it through the window, and with the barometer falling fast and the wind howling, he would lift the lid off the well house, arrange some kind of a tripod to support the light bulb, close up the well house, and with a happy thought for the financial assistance we were giving the local power company, he would return (soaking wet and cold) to his home and hearth. . . .

"If it *does* freeze, we won't have one single drop of water in the morning."

He yawned. "The wind is coming from the east, not from the north. It's raining. Never freezes when it rains. Let's go to bed."

"Ed, seriously . . ."

"For crying out loud! This is November, not January! I *promise* you the well pump won't freeze."

I slept soundly, and did not know when the rain ceased and the wind shifted. The alarm rang at 6:45. I got up quickly, closed the window and moved sleepily toward the kitchen to start the coffee.

In his usual predawn search for the last cigarette in the house, Ed followed me, so he was standing next to me when I held the percolator under the water tap and turned it on.

There was a short gulping sound, an odd lack of resistance to the handle, as if it might fall off into my hand, and no water, not even a drop.

I turned toward my husband, the barren coffeepot in my hand.

"Don't say a word! Don't say a word!" he instructed. "I was wrong. I admit it. But you'll have water, all the water you want. I'll get it for you." He grinned and added, "Cheerfully."

The shop in Snoqualmie was connected with a municipal water system which was not vulnerable to the assault of freezing temperatures as was our private well and well pump at home. An hour before dawn, Ed began his first trip with a load of empty vinegar jugs and kerosene cans and thermos bottles.

It was four and a half miles each way, and the roads were coated with ice. Again and again, he filled the jugs and cans at the sink in the *Record* office, carried them out to the car, crawled home with them, emptied the cargo into laundry tubs and cooking utensils and the bathtubs, and crawled back. Six round trips of about ten miles each, at intervals all day long, and as he had promised, he made them cheerfully. About seven o'clock he turned out the shop lights, locked the office door, and got into the car for the one-way trip which was to end the back-breaking day.

The temperature had been rising steadily, melting all but a few patches of ice. Ground that had sparkled in the morning with crystals of frost had been converted into soft, gluey mud.

Driving home in the dark, Ed took one hand off the

wheel so as to grope for a package of cigarettes. His fingers located the package, but not the matches. He pushed the cigarette lighter, waited with the cold cigarette between his lips. The lighter didn't pop out. Stuck? Burning? He looked down to see.

It wasn't a serious accident. A patch of ice, a soft shoulder, and the car skidded off the road into a shallow ditch, where the tires spun futilely in pockets of mud.

It was a hard test for a man determined to be cheerful. He walked a quarter-mile to the nearest house, called a wrecker, walked back to the car and waited in the cold for twenty minutes. By the time the wrecker arrived, his determination was slipping and the driver did nothing to renew it when he barked, "Say, what you got all them gallon jugs in the back seat for?"

"For peace and quiet!" Ed snapped, paid five dollars for his deliverance and drove home.

When he came into the kitchen, he was smiling, but the expression fit his face the way a left shoe fits a right foot. I watched him uneasily as he walked into the living room with an armload of papers; he moved too briskly, as if he were doing it under doctor's orders.

Back in the kitchen, he asked, "Where's John? Where's Hi? They can help me bring in the water."

"John's in his room. I'll call him. Hi hasn't come home yet."

"What! It's eight o'clock!"

"I'm sure he's all right. . . ."

There was more of an explanation than that. The *Seattle Times* was conducting a subscription drive. Hi had been trying for one of the alluring bonus prizes, and hadn't come home before eight o'clock for several nights in a row. Ed didn't know this, for he'd been even later getting home from work, and in his present mood I didn't want to tell him.

"Johnny?" I called. "Come help Dad unload the car."

"Did he telephone?" Ed demanded. "Did he let you know he'd be late?"

"Please don't worry. There's no need to. . . ."

Ed brought a fist down on the counter in a gesture of helpless rage. "It's a dark night. It's cold. That kid has no business out alone on a bike on a night like this!"

Johnny had come into the kitchen and he was watching his father with troubled blue eyes. In the silence which followed Ed's ultimatum, Johnny said timidly, "Hi's here now, Dad. I saw his bike light coming up our drive."

Apprehension settled in a tight, cold knot in my chest. I started forward and nervously placed a hand on Ed's arm. "Ed, don't be harsh with the boy. Don't say something you'll wish you hadn't said."

I only made him angrier. Now it wasn't a simple question of discipline. Now he had to prove to me that he was the head of the family, that he had a right to punish his children, and moreover to decide how harsh that punishment should be.

He freed his arm, walked across the kitchen to the back door. Opening it, he called, "Get in here, Hi!"

"He has to put his bicycle up," I said hurriedly, "and bring the carrying bags inside so they will dry out."

"Get in here right now!" Ed shouted. Again, I'd made things worse.

But I couldn't seem to stop myself. "Please," I begged him. "Relax. Wait a minute. Give him a chance . . ."

Hi came into the kitchen. The light was bright and his glasses were wet with rain. Squinting at his father, he asked, "What is it, Dad?"

"You tell me. Where have you been?"

Hi looked at his father defiantly. "Selling subscriptions to the *Times*."

"Until eight o'clock at night? No dinner? Practically no lights on your bike?"

"I've got a brand new light, Dad. A good one. And I don't mind eating late."

"You don't mind. It's your mother who has to go to extra trouble so that you can eat whenever it's convenient for you."

I caught my breath. It isn't fair! I thought. You can't use me as the reason for a scolding I didn't want and tried to prevent. "It's no trouble at all," I said shakily, near to tears. "In any case, I haven't been holding dinner just for Hi, but for you, too."

Ed ignored me. "I don't care to argue, Hi. I recognize that the paper route has been a good thing for you, in some ways. But I want you to give it up."

"Dad . . ."

"I said I don't want to argue!"

Blinking rapidly behind lenses fogged with rain, Hi said stubbornly, "I can't drop it just like that—I'm the dealer. I've sold a lot of people subscriptions and it's up to me to deliver them."

"You aren't under contract."

"I don't care whether I am or not, Dad. I've got a—well, I've got an obligation."

No word could have hurt his father more. Obligation? There was only one, and that was to the family enterprise which through love and labor Ed had built and held together. He stared at our older son with such naked distress in his face that I had to look away. "They can find someone else," he said at last. "And you have a substitute, don't you? Some boy who knows the route already? He can take over for you."

Hi didn't answer. There was a long, curious silence as he removed his glasses and dried them on a handkerchief he pulled from the rear pocket of his blue jeans. He seemed to be waiting.

Johnny cleared his throat, threw Hi a despairing look, and turned to face his father. "Dad, I signed up to be Hi's sub."

Silence. A long, throbbing silence.

Johnny continued anxiously, "I thought it would be all right. Since Hi was allowed to. I was going to tell Mom first . . ."

Ed turned to me. "If you don't mind," he said quietly, "I think I'll go right to bed."

"You haven't eaten. I'll get some supper. . . ."

He shook his head. "Get it for Hi." He walked out of the kitchen, and a few minutes later I heard the bedroom door close behind him.

Smoky, I thought, Smoky, don't close the door. But of course it was closed already.

iv

The mechanical department of the Falls Printing Company was back at full strength much sooner than Ed had anticipated. Bob limped, but as Don put it, he limped awful fast, and Don was soon using the aluminum guard on his right hand as if it were a standard tool of the printing trade.

Even the new Linotype operator, hired by mail to replace the hard-drinking compositor Bart Luther, was proving to be a good employee. He was sober. He had no vice other than playing pinball machines. But most important, his bowling average was nearly 200. As Thanksgiving approached, the Falls Printing Company was leading the Merchants' League, the *Record* was coming out on time, and Ed's work week was reduced to proportions which, by comparison, amounted to a life of sweet repose. It was prosperity, to which Ed immediately paid tribute by breaking out with shingles.

There are worse ailments than shingles, but none which takes possession of the sufferer so completely. This was especially true of Ed because he had gone through the experience before. The pains of childbirth are soon forgotten, perhaps because of the lively bonus awarded when it's all over, but the only prize for having shingles is the relief of having them end, and the sensation of living inside a body every inch of which is either burning or itching is not lightly dismissed from the mind.

The morning Ed told me he'd slept poorly because he "felt tingly all over," I knew what was coming. Like all repeaters, he was cursed with painful memories of past suffering. It would be no good telling him to relax, because an old pro at shingles won't, and can't, until he's gone and done it again. At last the itching, burning clusters erupt. There is relief, even exultation, in his voice as he reveals the first raw, red torture area. He *knew* this would happen, and it has. He has been justified. . . .

Perhaps it was an improvement on his earlier cases, but this time Ed broke out without any such preliminaries. "Business has never been better," he said at the dinner table, and the next morning he was covered with shingles, head to toe.

I filled the bathtub with warm water and laced it with the colloidal oatmeal which a doctor had suggested the year before. Ed soaked in this nutritious ooze until the water was cold, and came out itching as badly as before. We tried various ointments prescribed by the three different dermatologists. I smeared him with jars of homemade remedies contributed by compassionate *Record* subscribers. Nothing cured him, and Hi's weekly column, The Hi-Corner, consisted of just one sentence: "I didn't get around to a column this week on account of my Dad has the shingles."

That brief notice brought Ed the first real relief. It came from our friend Hi Wallace, a retired farmer. It had been years since he'd done any slaughtering or cutting, but he still put his faith in meat. When he read our son Hi's Hi-Corner, he drove twenty miles from his farm to our house to deliver a tremendous piece of beefsteak.

Ed surveyed the meat through swollen eyelids. "That's a lot of meat," he moaned, "but it still won't cover me."

"It goes on the inside, my friend, not on the outside." Big Hi gave the massive tenderloin a loving pat. "It's a nice piece. A real nice piece. We've been eating on it some ourselves."

No ointment, potion or sedative did as much to soothe Ed's stricken periphery as did Dr. Wallace's prescription. It may even have been the cure, for the next day Ed was so much improved he got out of bed, went to the type-writer in the living room and composed this editorial for the *Record*: "Shingles," he wrote, "are about to stop giving the aging editor the shakes for this semester. . . ."

For a week I had hardly seen Hi and John except at breakfast and supper. Involved with oatmeal baths and ointments, I had been an absent-minded mother at best. When their father felt well enough to attend an evening meeting, the boys and I were alone for the first time in a week, and they approached me like a pair of bailiffs.

Hi said, "Mom, could we sit down and talk to you about something?"

We took chairs at the old oak dining-room table in the middle of the living room.

"The thing we were wondering about," Hi said, "is whether Dad ever answered the letter from that man in California."

I had the sensation that we were repeating a scene we'd rehearsed before. Hi was determined, even grim. Johnny was uneasy but game. "Apparently you've overheard some conversation between me and Dad."

"Yes, we have."

"If you're going to eavesdrop, do it thoroughly."

"Mom," Johnny protested, "we couldn't hear everything you said!"

Hi looked at me squarely. "From what I heard, Dad has no intention of writing to the man."

"That's right."

"That's why we wanted to talk to you. We think you ought to tell Dad to sell the paper."

Silently I gave thanks for the fact that Ed was miles away. I felt as if I were holding something very fragile and very valuable and it was up to me to set it down some place without breaking it.

"I don't *tell* your father anything. I wouldn't even if I thought I could."

"All right, Mom, I used the wrong word. I should have said that Johnny and I wish you would *urge* Dad to sell."

"Tell me why."

"There are two reasons." Hi pushed his glasses up onto the bridge of his short nose, held up his left hand and pushed the first finger down with his right hand. "One. Dad's health. He says he's fine now, but he just got over another case of shingles and if he stays in this business he might have another heart attack. Two . . ." He bent the second finger forward. "Two, I think the reason he won't talk to anyone about selling the paper is that he figures John and I will take it over when we're out of college."

"He's always said you boys are free to choose your own fields."

Hi nodded solemnly. "He *says* that, Mom. But tell me honestly—do you think he means it?"

I knew better than Hi that he didn't. How wide the gap is between what we say and earnestly believe we mean, and what we really feel!

"You're only thirteen years old, John's only twelve. It's years before you'll make up your minds about what you want to do."

"That's just *it*, Mom, that's just what we're trying to tell you. Dad is fifty. It isn't right for him to hold onto the paper for all that time before we decide if we want to run it."

"The way you feel now, you definitely do not?"

Both boys were silent.

"Johnny?"

"I hope you won't feel bad, Mom. I know it sounds silly, because I'll probably never be good enough, but I really would like to be a baseball player."

"Hi?"

"I'm interested in newspaper work. But not on a weekly, Mom. I'd like to get a job on a big daily newspaper and work up to being a foreign correspondent."

Boys of twelve and thirteen years need not be taken too seriously. A shortstop with a major league, an American in Paris or Cairo or Berlin . . . These daydreams did not disturb me. Hi's earlier statement did.

Why *should* Ed continue for ten or twelve years in a business that had almost killed him, when neither of his sons wanted any more part of it than Mr. Frank Harvey's son wanted in his father's orange groves? The big man from California knew of his son's defection. He had faced it, accepted it. Ed had not.

"Dad's just beginning to feel better," I said, consciously playing for time. "Besides, you might very well change your minds. You should think about it longer."

Hi said in a husky voice, "I guess you don't know how much I *have* been thinking about it. Maybe I won't get to be a foreign correspondent. Whatever I do, it's going to be my job. I'm going to do it on my own."

"Don't you realize that that is the very feeling your father had so strongly that he left Chicago and came out here to buy this business of our own?"

"Then why doesn't he want me to feel that way, too?"

"He *does* understand. He was angry last week, but he let you keep your paper route, didn't he?"

"Yes."

"More than that, he's helped you with your route."

"I didn't want any help."

"Maybe not, Hi," I said quietly, "but you were awfully glad to have it when Dad insisted."

Hi looked down. "I guess so."

"Don't forget it. He bawled you out that night because he was worried about you, and very tired. He's been coöperative about your paper route even when it has kept you from helping him at the shop."

"It just seems like . . ." Hi shook his head, searching for the words, and finally murmured, "Sometimes it seems like he's jealous of my job."

My heart contracted. The old buck and the young. Jealousy and rebellion.

Johnny brought us back to the subject and saved me from answering Hi. "Then you *aren't* going to tell Dad we think he should sell the *Record*?"

"Let's wait a little while."

Blue-eyed practical Johnny said, "If you wait too long to talk to Dad, maybe that man from California will buy some other newspaper."

"I'll wait a little while," I countered, "just a little while. Sometime the subject will come up, the right time to discuss it . . ."

But I knew better. There never could be a right time.

7

FROM THE MOMENT we bought a weekly newspaper in the Snoqualmie Valley, we were all in business together. "The four of us," Ed would remark proudly whenever we were all working in the shop at the same time, though the four chairmen of the board were more often than not occupying themselves like a team of four janitors. The single source of pride greater than all others, and a symbol of the four-way sharing which meant so much to him, was the fact that we all wrote weekly columns for the *Record*.

Ed's was an unconventional editorial in the conventional upper left corner of the editorial page; it was called EDitorially Speaking. My column focused on subjects of interest to women. Hi celebrated his ninth birthday two or three weeks after he'd begun writing a weekly column which appeared at the upper left corner on the front page, appropriately entitled The Hi-Corner.

Hi had asked to write for the *Record*. It was an excited eight-year-old who begged his father to let him try and who could hardly believe his ears when Ed agreed. At the time Johnny was only seven years old, and not the most literary member of the second grade. Reading made him dizzy, he claimed; I suppose that was the reason he didn't indulge in it more often than was absolutely necessary. But when his older brother rose to the stature of a *Record* columnist, Johnny wanted his column, too.

"When you're older," Ed promised. "When you get over those dizzy spells."

We often discussed the column John would write some day. We felt—Ed more strongly than I—that when the youngest of the four of us began to write for our newspapers, the family partnership would reach a wholeness such as we'd never achieved before. The subject? For John, there could be only one. Sports.

Kindergarten took only three hours out of a day, and therefore did not interfere too seriously with more important concerns, but from the first grade on it was clear that Johnny considered book learning a pointless diversion of hours that could profitably be spent on basketball, baseball, tennis, golf, bowling, fishing, badminton or touch football.

"He used to get an 'A' in Sandbox," Ed remarked. "Now he's got a four-point average in Recess."

"He's a bright boy," I insisted. "He just hasn't found himself."

Ed chuckled. "Maybe not, but he sure seemed to know where he was on the baseball diamond this afternoon."

Since dressing up (i.e., wearing something besides blue jeans, a jersey and tennis shoes) was in Johnny's philosophy as profitless as reading books and getting dizzy, he didn't go to Sunday School regularly until a "church baseball league" was formed. Six churches in the Valley fielded teams. There were uniforms, practice sessions, weekly games, play-offs, trophies, and so forth. A boy's aptitude for the sport was not important, but there was one rigid requirement: A player who missed Sunday School could not suit up the following week. If his family took him on a week-end excursion, he was to attend church or Sunday School (of any denomination) in the area they visited.

No unusual degree of sensitivity was necessary to observe that my son's piety ceased abruptly with the close of the baseball season and picked up again just as suddenly when the church basketball league was organized in the fall. In April he'd been so devout that he wouldn't go to the beach for a week end until we'd promised to take him to the nearest church on Sunday morning. In July and August, it seemed that organized religion made him as dizzy as reading. In November, he dusted off his Bible *and* his knee pads.

"To me, it's all wrong," I complained to Ed. "He's doing a good thing for a bad reason."

"Basketball isn't bad."

"No, of course not. Neither is baseball. But he shouldn't be going to Sunday School simply to remain eligible to play."

Ed smiled. "Maybe he's praying for the team."

"Don't be irreverent. You know perfectly well that while everyone else is singing hymns or reading psalms, Johnny's thinking about a fast double play or a full court press."

"Lutherans, Congregationalists, Catholics, or Methodists, there are a lot of boys like John. Do you suppose he's the only boy in the church league whose spiritual life is the by-product of a ball game?"

I said primly, "Well, our son is going to learn the meaning of integrity."

Ed smiled. "Oh shades of Boston. For Johnny's sake, I hope your high principles won't get out of hand until he's played a couple more games."

I might never have taken action if it were not for a week-end trip which had us on a ferryboat during the hours Johnny should have "made up" Sunday School at some church along the way.

"We won't get off the boat until 12:30!" Johnny cried when he saw the schedule. "Can't we take a later boat, or an earlier boat, or something?"

"I'm sorry, John. We've missed the earlier ferries, and the afternoon sailings would make us much too late getting home."

"Mom! If I don't go to Sunday School some place, I won't be allowed to play in the game Saturday. Mom, it's with the *Lutherans!*"

I shook my head. "I thought we could arrange it, but it's impossible."

And then he asked the question which convinced me it was time to talk about integrity. "There's four of us here in the car," he said triumphantly. "Can't we have a Quaker meeting?"

The most enthusiastic fans at the church league games were the ministers, and wives of the ministers, of the sponsoring churches. "Kill the ump!" the gentle Baptist pastor would shout at the officiating Congregationalist cleric. Fifty years ago an itinerant Methodist preacher in our Valley was widely admired (among other reasons) for his ability to drive an ox team without using one word of the language oxen knew best. At every baseball and basketball game our present-day ministers matched his remarkable feat. They yelled, paced the sidelines, threw their hats on the ground and walked on them, cheered for one side and shook their fists at the other, but they never uttered a word beyond "Pshaw!" or "Rats!"

The pastor of the church Johnny attended was one of those who never missed a game. In the *Record* office one afternoon he asked why Johnny had not appeared for the last basketball game.

"Because I won't let him go to Sunday School."

The minister stared. "What do you mean?"

"The only reason he was attending was to be eligible for the team. He should go to Sunday School because it's important in itself, not because of some sports activity."

"Oh you parents!" the minister groaned. "We poor preachers knock ourselves out to think of some way we can get youngsters inside a church and then you come along and spoil everything. What difference does it make *why* Johnny goes to Sunday School? As long as he goes, he'll get something out of it."

"You really believe I should let him, even when I know he'll quit just as soon as the basketball season is over?"

"Maybe he won't."

"Well, all right. But I'll bet there will be quite a few moments when he hasn't got his mind on the text."

The pastor smiled. "That could happen," he said quietly, "to almost anyone."

As the wise minister predicted, Johnny did not drop out of Sunday School after the last league game. Sports and religion did mix. Not so sports and love.

John was in the sixth grade when he asked permission to buy a girl a ring. He approached us so solemnly that Ed and I straightened up like Supreme Court justices holding an emergency hearing in the kitchen.

A "friendship ring," Johnny explained, did not mean the wearer or donor was going steady. He also assured us that Mitzi was a good girl, a statement which raised the interesting question of what else a girl might be in the sixth grade. *And* he would pay for the ring with his own money.

Ed stood up and hurried toward the living room.

"Where are you going?" I demanded.

"Phone call," he mumbled. "I'll concur with—the—uh—majority opinion."

The next afternoon Johnny walked to town where he

purchased a ring for a dollar. He'd forgotten about the three-and-a-half percent sales tax and the ten percent luxury tax but the jeweler let him open a charge account and the next afternoon he walked to town again to pay the fourteen-cent balance.

The affair had its difficulties from the first, for Mitzi liked to write letters. One, which I found later and read shamelessly, ran as follows:

Dear John,

Thanks for dancing with me Wed. It was a lot of fun. I want to tell you in my own words that "I like you a lot." But you don't have to like me if you don't want to. But I sure would like it if you would like me. Now that I wrote a letter to you, will you write a letter back? Do you like the story Eskimo Families? Please write me a letter? It doesn't have to be long but it will be a good letter to me. I would like to get one from you. What's your favorite subject? I like geography and spelling. Who's your best friend? Mine is Sue Ann, most of the time. Well, I better say Goodbye.

With love very much,
/s/ Mitzi Holdrith

P.S. PLEASE WRITE BACK

Another P.S. My address is written on the back of this.

Johnny didn't seem to mind receiving Mitzi's letters, prejudiced as he was against reading of any sort, but when Mitzi insisted he answer, Johnny balked.

The crisis came during a recess when Mitzi offered him an envelope, which she said was a new letter from her. John reached for it, Mitzi jerked it out of his hand and hid it behind her back.

"All right," John retorted. "I don't care if I do see it. I don't care much for letters, anyway."

This was cruel scorn to Mitzi, who had been pouring her heart out three or four times a week. She kicked him.

John didn't back away or say "Ouch" so ⟨...⟩
would have done it again if John hadn't p⟨...⟩
with an arm. The round ended right the⟨...⟩
of the teachers moved in, charged Johnny ⟨...⟩
girl, and ordered him confined to his classro⟨...⟩
recesses for the next two weeks.

The teacher who interrupted the fight wa⟨...⟩ ⟨...⟩
favorite, an extremely pretty young woman in w...ose eyes
he wanted very much to appear honorable and manly.
When he described the incident at home that evening he
wasn't nearly as disturbed by the fact that for two weeks
he wouldn't be allowed to go outside during recess as he
was by the shame of having this particular teacher think
he'd been a cad.

"Write the teacher a letter," Ed suggested.

"Do you think that would be O.K. to do?"

"The girls at your school seem to go for letters," his
father said wryly. "Sure, go ahead."

So John wrote, and Ed solemnly approved, the following message:

Dear Miss S.:

I wanted to tell you that I did not hit Mitzi. You
thought I did because I raised my left hand to gard the
punches.

This letter is to you and not for you to give to my
teacher to read to the class just in case you were going to
do that.

I haven't hit a girl for a long time and I don't want to
hit one now.

Sincerely,
/s/ John Groshell

P.S. I am not trying to get to go out at recess.

A few days later I was digging through the irreplace-
able treasure on top of Johnny's chest of drawers. At the
bottom, under a heavy layer of bubble gum premium base-

cards, was the $1.14 friendship ring. I put it back, replaced the baseball cards and the golf tees, badminton birds, nylon fishing line, and marble bag which had been lying on top of them, topped the mound with a catcher's mitt, and crept away.

Hi was a seasoned writer of four years' experience and John was eleven and a half years old when the circle of Groshell columnists was finally closed. John's Sports Shorts was the name of the weekly feature authored by our younger son.

"You understand that you'll have to write a column every week, not simply when you happen to feel like it?"

John said earnestly that he understood.

Ed continued, "And you know you'll have to meet a deadline? Six o'clock Monday evening, even if there's a game that day?"

"I do," Johnny vowed.

"If we start running your column, we have to keep it up. It won't always be fun, but it will always be work. Are you sure you're ready to accept that sort of responsibility?"

John said solemnly, "Sure I'm sure."

Thus the yoke of the weekly deadline was dropped on his young shoulders, and he joined the rest of us in the great dilemma—what to write about? We soon noted that these problems disturbed him far less than Hi.

Johnny put off writing until quarter to six, then picked up the nearest scratch pad, dashed off his opinions on the National League pennant or the School District 410 marble tournament, and met the deadline with thirty seconds to spare. Hi took notes, studied them, discussed the subject with me, argued about it with his father, and finally spent an hour at his typewriter in a dogged attempt to turn out a page of copy without one single typographical error.

Hi's instructions were to express a boy's point of view on any subject at all, preferably in connection with a project or event of local interest. This assignment, being so free, was also difficult. "Write about anything at all" sounds wonderful to the mature writer but to a boy it means "I don't have anything to write about."

Hi editorialized in support of the March of Dimes, and the campaign to bring the Seattle Symphony orchestra to the Valley; he reported the views of his contemporaries on summer jobs, comic books and Christmas presents; he interviewed a candidate for the town council and the cook at the grade school cafeteria. But every week he had to go through the same burdensome search, while the younger, fresher writer of John's Sports Shorts always knew exactly what to write about: Sports.

There were always games, some place. John simply picked the one closest to home, wrote what he knew and thought about it with a minimum of words, and left big issues to his older brother.

John and Hi got more encouragement from *Record* readers than did their mother and father. But we expected that. Years before, when Hi was in the fifth grade and Johnny hadn't begun to write a column, we had learned how easily the senior columnists could be displaced.

The United Good Neighbors organization was about to launch its annual drive. In order to acquaint newspaper editors and feature writers with a few of the facilities supported by the fund, the publicity director organized a tour. Three institutions were to be visited: A dormitory and delousing center for men on Seattle's skid road, a boarding school for mentally disturbed children, and a home for wayward girls. The invitation to join the tour was addressed to Hi.

I telephoned immediately. "There must be some confusion about names. The editor and publisher is *Ed Groshell*."

"Oh, he can come along if he wants to," the publicity director assured me. "But I wanted to be sure that the writer of The Hi-Corner would be with us."

"He's only eleven years old!"

"Well, it's up to you, of course. But the best publicity, for us, is an article we know everyone will read."

I accompanied Hi, primarily as chauffeur to and from UGN headquarters in Seattle. During the tour Hi asked the questions and took the notes. The others in the group were veteran newspapermen, reporters, feature writers, editors, who had been working on metropolitan dailies for a good deal longer than Hi had been alive. Hi took his place among them without apology or self-consciousness. When they sat down for a press conference in the director's office, Hi took a chair among the reporters, and I sat in the corner.

Only once was he obviously shocked. We were inspecting the delousing station, where a half dozen battered wayfarers wrapped in blankets were sitting on a bench while their clothing was being processed.

"After they're washed," the deaconess in charge explained with a gesture which seemed to indicate the men, "we put them into this room here"—and she opened the door to a windowless, oven-hot tank—"where the temperature is 300 to 325 degrees. We leave them there for an hour."

"You *do!*" Hi exclaimed, and perhaps it was just as well that I'd gone with him, because I whispered, "The clothes, not the men" before he could say something more and thus lose face before his elders.

At the home for delinquent girls I was useful, too, at least for a moment or two. As we walked into the building I took Hi aside.

"Hi," I said quietly, "I know one question you're bound to ask: What did these girls do to get in here? We haven't

time to discuss it now, but would you do me a favor? Hold
that question until later. I'm not trying to keep anything
from you. Later, O.K.?"

"Sure, Mom," he whispered reassuringly, but it sounded
as if he were the one who had a few things to explain
to me.

After the tour the United fund personnel returned us to
their headquarters where we'd left our cars. One of the
newspapermen walked up to Hi and extended his hand.

"I want to shake hands with you, boy," he said. "You
handled yourself like a pro."

"Gee, thanks a lot."

"Since your Dad started a newspaper in North Bend, as
well as in Snoqualmie, you represent two *Records*."

"Well, yes, I guess I do."

"I couldn't have done it at your age. By the time you're
twenty-one or two, you'll take those newspapers away
from your father and he'll be out of a job. Tell him I
said so."

"I don't figure on staying in Snoqualmie or North Bend."

"Sure you do. You've got two good newspapers. I know
because I see them quite frequently. You might not think
so now, but you'll end up going into business with your
old man."

"No, sir," Hi said firmly. "No, I don't want to do that."

The older man laughed. "Isn't that always the way . . . ?"

If Ed had heard the conversation, he might have laughed
indulgently. He might have said, like the Seattle man,
"Isn't that always the way . . . ?" Nevertheless, I was
very glad he had not come on the tour.

An eleven-year-old boy is a long way from manhood,
I reasoned. Hi may very well change. The uneasy feeling
that brief conversation had given me lasted only a day or
so. Within a year there was another, more serious sign of
defection.

At long last, we were all columnists for our newspapers. Ed's pride, only three-quarters fulfilled until Johnny joined the ranks, was now complete. But Hi had been writing The Hi-Corner for four years. The weekly deadline was becoming irksome to him, and he was entering the age when life's worst hazards are the questions, "What will people think?" and "What will people say?"

"Dad, who cares about that?" he objected when Ed suggested that for The Hi-Corner's fourth anniversary he write a history of the column.

Ed frowned. "Who cares? The Hi-Corner is the most popular feature we have. That's not meant to take away from Johnny's column. He's only just started, and a great many people have been reading your column for years. Newspapermen all over the state think it's a good feature, too, or you wouldn't have received that press club award."

"That was two years ago. When I was just a kid."

Ed said patiently, "Of course you're older now, but you're writing a better column now than you were then."

"You don't know what the kids at school say!"

Ed shook his head slowly. "No, I don't."

"Just about every week someone at school bawls me out for what I wrote, or laughs at me. Or else someone says what I wrote was all wrong."

"For every boy or girl who teases you at school, there are a hundred men and women who think your column is the best thing in the *Valley Record*."

"Dad, I don't go to school with them."

"Do you think the kids who criticize you are right?"

"No. It's usually someone who's mad because I mentioned some other kid's name and didn't put in hers."

"Well?" Ed looked thoughtfully at our beleaguered eighth grader. "To whom are you responsible? To the hundreds of readers who look for your column every week or to the girl or boy who tries to tear you down?"

The only "right" answer was contained in the question. Hi murmured, "O.K., Dad," and went to his room. When he and John came home from school Monday afternoon, Hi brought me a finished column. "This is one week you can't say I turned it in late. John hasn't even started his."

I glanced at the sheet of copy. "You've written about the basketball tournament."

"Before John started his column you let me write about sports."

"We 'let' you, of course, but you seldom wanted to, even when we suggested it." I could have added, *Especially* when we suggested it.

"Well, John said he's going to write about the hockey league. So that leaves basketball and anyway there's nothing else to write about."

I shook my head. "Hi, you aren't being honest. Yesterday Dad made a good suggestion for this week's subject. And you agreed to write it."

"You talk about being honest! *I* didn't agree. You *knew* I didn't. I just didn't try to argue with Dad, that's all."

I was shocked at the quality of bitterness in such a young voice. "Don't be disrespectful . . ." I murmured, looking down at the article he'd written.

"I'm sorry."

"We've never forced you to write on any subject."

"No. But you know as well as I do how Dad feels if I don't follow what he calls a suggestion."

"That's true. But something else is true, too. You often turn down a suggestion just to prove you don't have to follow it."

He wasn't to be disrespectful. He wasn't to argue. And he was too old to cry. But he was choking with unhappiness and rebellion. "Mom," he said stiffly, "how long do I have to keep on writing my column?"

The old phrases leaped into my mind. Don't bother

Dad. Let's not talk about it right now. We'll discuss it another time. . . . "You don't even have to think about it for a week."

"No, seriously. How long does Dad expect me to keep up The Hi-Corner?"

"Oh, Hi," I said uncomfortably. "I don't know. I doubt that Dad has ever thought that on such and such a date you'd stop writing a column."

"I'm going to ask him."

It was a challenge, not to his father, to me. He was saying, I'm going to fight him and you'd better get out of the way. . . . I said quietly, "Dad will be terribly disappointed."

"If he says I have to keep writing it, I will. But I'm going to ask!"

It was the asking that would hurt. The loss of Hi's column would be nothing compared to the loss of Hi's interest in writing it. Should I try to explain that to the boy, or did he know it as well as I? What does it matter, I thought wearily, whether the boy hurts his father knowingly or unknowingly? "All right, Hi. But remember that writing a column was your own idea. You *asked* to do it."

"You and Dad have reminded me about that a hundred times." Pushing himself to the brink of disrespect, he added stubbornly, "It seems as if you don't know that anything ever changes."

I dreaded the moment Hi would choose to question his father about The Hi-Corner, but it was postponed, thanks to the State Highway Department.

A telephone call came that evening from the night foreman of a crew of men who work on the highway at Snoqualmie Pass, the divide in the Cascades which lies 3500 feet above and some eighteen miles to the east of the Snoqualmie Valley floor.

"No, I don't want to talk to Ed," said Bill Francis, the foreman. "I want to talk to Hi."

"Hi? Our son?"

"Yes. The fellow who writes that article on the front page of the paper every week."

I handed the receiver to the author of The Hi-Corner, who said in a squeaky voice, "Yes, uh, sir?"

An earlier Hi-Corner had described a trip Hi made to the summit with the sergeant in charge of the Snoqualmie Pass detachment of the state patrol. Mr. Francis felt that the State Highway Department did an equally important job and should receive equal recognition. Not through an editorial by the *Record's* publisher, nor through a feature article by the publisher's wife. He wanted Hi to go up to the pass with him some night and write an article for The Hi-Corner describing a shift with the highway crews.

"Yes, sir, I'd like to," Hi replied. Ed, Johnny and I were sitting at the kitchen table, listening with rapt interest. Glancing toward us, Hi added quickly, "Mr. Francis, would it be all right if I brought my brother and my parents?"

That Saturday night all four Groshells—two columnists and two tourists—rode with Bill Francis to Snoqualmie Pass. We arrived about eleven o'clock. For an hour Hi interviewed radio operators and other members of the highway crew, taking notes on a scratch pad which was heavily adorned on the outside by original drawings of unlimited hydroplanes. At midnight, he and John went on shift.

For two hours they rode with men operating the huge roto-blade "snow blows," which grind a path through a hundred inches of snow like a drill biting into wood. The cab of the giant snow-eater was warm, the world outside was endlessly white, the vibration of the roto blades and the swish of flying snow was loud and hypnotic. At 2:00

A.M. the driver pulled up in front of Highway Department headquarters and delivered the columnists, who woke up just enough to stumble inside without help from anyone.

That week The Hi-Corner filled a column and brought Hi a note of thanks from Bill Francis and several congratulatory telephone calls from other *Record* readers. Hi and I were alone in the kitchen after a particularly enthusiastic subscriber had telephoned.

After the call Hi whispered to me, "Did you have that talk with Dad? You know, about what we were talking about?"

"About how long he expects you to continue writing your column?"

"Yes."

"No, I haven't said anything to him. I thought you were going to."

"Well, I will sometime. But I'll wait for a while. I'm still in grade school, so I guess . . ." He shrugged. "Well, I just wanted to say, don't you bother to ask him either."

Silently, I thanked Bill Francis. Hi's urgent need to prove he wasn't too young, Ed's responding need to show he wasn't too old—peace be with us, the locking of horns had been postponed. I called, "Wash up for supper!" and reached for the serving spoon. In a moment father and sons were tranquilly viewing the casserole, united, at least temporarily, in their appreciation of beef with noodles. There was no reason, now, for my hand to be shaking so.

ii

It was Wednesday morning, "Paper Day," when the last press run completed that week's edition of the *Record* and our friendly tenant, the Snoqualmie postmaster, performed the final act of the five-day ritual called "getting-out-the-paper."

Ed set his alarm clock for 5:30. It was a fiendish invention which flashed a light instead of ringing a bell, and it was supposed to rouse him without disturbing me, but the silent and terrible glare bored through my closed eyelids and I was awake before he was.

"Go back to sleep," he said groggily as he groped for his slippers and robe. He kissed me, and left the room quietly.

I wanted to obey him. The outside world was cold, dark, and demanding; six hours' sleep had not prepared me for it. I lay very still, and tried to retreat into sleep. Ed finished in the bath, moved quietly through the living room to the kitchen. Faintly I heard the controlled opening and closing of the back door, and then he started the car and drove away.

Hi and John wouldn't get up for two hours. I must relax, I must sleep. But my body remained tense, defeating me; pledged, I thought irritably, to the waste of two precious hours. On the luminous dial of my little bedside clock, the minute hand moved doggedly along its course. Fifteen, twenty, twenty-five minutes. Nettled at my failure, I threw back the covers and stood up.

The movement stirred a pain so sharp I gasped and sat down on the edge of the bed. It was in my right hip, the silly little ache suddenly gone wild. Like a burning electric current it shot from the hip socket to the knee, through the calf, to the foot. I waited a minute, then got to my feet carefully.

Each step released a jolt of pain, but I could walk. Inching into every necessary movement, I washed, dressed, and went into the kitchen. If I favored the right leg, throwing my weight onto the left leg whenever I stood still, I could move about naturally, at least without attracting attention. I measured coffee, filled the percolator, and lowered myself gratefully onto a chair to wait while the coffee brewed.

There was no doubt left. Any woman could find reasons for ignoring a chronic ache which at worst did no more than grate on the nerves or spoil a night's sleep. Only a foolish woman would try to deny the tearing pain I'd just experienced. I'd have to see the doctor.

But it was Wednesday. Paper Day. I cupped my hands around a mug of coffee, lifted it to my mouth and sipped at the rim. Paper Day was often a long, nerve-shredding day, for interruptions which could be absorbed by Monday's or Tuesday's routine were not easily assimilated when the mailing deadline was only three or four hours away.

Life in a small town had not always coöperated with the overburdened publisher of the *Record*. One press day years before, a former owner had been called from his job to help three men subdue a townsman on the street outside the *Record* office. The man had cut his throat but resented their efforts to take him to the hospital.

With a quick eye the editor saw that if someone didn't hold the man while someone else drove the car, he was going to lose a paid-up subscriber and would suffer the additional embarrassment of having a prominent local personality bleed to death on the steps of his newspaper shop. So he joined the struggle and went along to the hospital, battling every foot of the way to keep the demented man from clawing at his throat with his fingers. He hurried back from the hospital, raced to the *Record's* production line, and the paper came out on time, though he wouldn't have made it, he mentioned delicately, if he'd stopped to change his clothes.

Once in the history of the town, an elephant ran loose through Snoqualmie, and that, too, happened on Paper Day.

A circus had come to roost on a pasture to the north of

the main street, and sometime during the night the largest attraction broke from his moorings and like anyone on a toot, he headed straight for town.

Ed had gone to the shop about three o'clock that morning. At six he sat down in his office to pour a cup of coffee from the thermos he'd brought from home. A heavy thudding sound startled him. He looked up, and over the rim of the plastic coffee cup he stared at the building across the street, perfectly framed by the front and back legs and curving belly line of a very large elephant.

He set the cup down, and dialed our home telephone number. "Hello, hon?" he greeted me. "There's an elephant at the *Record* office."

"Did you hire him or did he stop by to pay his subscription?"

"Now he's going down the street toward the dairy." And Ed hung up.

That sounded real. The children were still asleep, so I ran to the battered sedan we'd purchased as a second car and drove as fast as it would travel to Snoqualmie.

By that time the elephant had reached the dairy at the end of the street and was circling back via the well-kept lawns and neat vegetable and flower gardens behind a block of houses, adjacent to the *Record* office. One clothesline had impeded him, but only for a few seconds; he was wearing it like a string of pearls when the men from the circus arrived. He had left footprints as big and deep as buckets in every yard between the dairy and the *Record* but otherwise he'd done little damage beyond waking up everyone in town thirty minutes before their alarms went off.

From a boy on a bicycle I learned that Ed had been on the scene, too, and I also got a brand-new idea of the prestige enjoyed by the editor.

"Which way did he go?" the boy shouted excitedly when he spotted me on the corner near our shop.

"That way. They got him tied up and they're taking him back to the circus."

"Not the elephant!" he protested. "Mr. Groshell! He's who I want to see."

On another eventful Paper Day, we almost missed mail time because two loggers were fighting only a few feet from the back door of the pressroom. The glass pane in this door offered an unexcelled (and protected) view of the proceedings, and until the town marshal arrived it was hard to get anyone interested in setting type or running a press.

One disputant was sitting on the other, pinning him to the gravel and shouting, "Get the marshal! Someone go get the marshal! I can't let him up or he'll kill me!"

Even with his wind cut off somewhat by the top man's knees, the man on the ground was able to explain what he planned to do the minute he was free, and it didn't sound good.

Our Linotype operator knew both men socially. "The one on the bottom is the husband," he told us cryptically.

The shouts must have been heard for two blocks in all directions but no one came forward to relieve Atlas of his burden until quiet-voiced, white-haired Mr. English, the druggist, passed by on his way to the post office.

Mr. English never left his store without the protection of a felt hat, which he wore straight across the forehead, giving his pink face a rather sweet, prim look. When the rose bushes were in bloom in front of the bank, he always paused there to pinch off the faded flowers, and then he would proceed across the street, one hand in the pocket of his starched gray pharmacist's jacket, the other resting on his chest and holding a packet of letters.

He nipped off the dead roses, as usual, then turned and

advanced at his usual measured pace until he was standing over the two fighters.

While a dozen muscular young men looked on from a safe distance (and the *Record's* staff pressed noses against the back door) Mr. English leaned down and asked politely, "What's the trouble?"

"Help me!" the man on top cried, emphasizing the urgency of the situation by driving one knee deeper into the other man's chest. "He's gone crazy. I gotta go find the marshal but I don't dare let him up."

"The marshal comes on duty at four o'clock," Mr. English advised.

"I'll go to his house and wake him up! Here, hold this guy for me till I get back."

Gentle and soft-voiced as he was, Mr. English was also more than six feet tall and weighed well over two hundred. "Certainly," he replied. He placed the packet of letters in the pocket of his pharmacist's coat and seated himself comfortably, as if the struggling, cursing body beneath him were his favorite easy chair. He immobilized the man's fists simply by gripping the wrists, using two hands for this exercise, except when he needed a free hand in order to take a clean handkerchief out of his pocket and blot his cheeks and chin.

The man the husband wanted to kill left town without bothering to summon the marshal. Eventually someone telephoned and Snoqualmie's policeman, who had been on patrol all night, appeared with sleep in his eyes and in mufti but willing and capable of performing his duty.

Mr. English got to his feet, said cordially, "How are you today, marshal?" and resumed his walk to the post office. His felt hat hadn't once been jarred out of position.

Our Linotype operator sighed, the printer rubbed his head, and they returned to the anticlimactic routine of Paper Day. . . .

The kitchen clock reminded me that it was time to wake up the boys. I got up stiffly, braced against a return of the pain. The movement of rising brought a shock, sharpest in the pit of the hip joint, echoed by the less painful throbbing sensation in my leg. When I began to walk, the feeling eased, and I thought—I'll wait until after Paper Day. I'll go to the doctor's tomorrow.

I went into Hi's room, and then Johnny's, and as soon as they were fully awake they began to watch me. It is not natural for teen-age boys to pay close attention to their mothers before breakfast. I turned to go back to the kitchen, and Hi asked, "You feeling O.K. today?"

John was more direct. "Hey, Mom, what's wrong with your leg?"

"Nothing much. Some kind of a little pain. I'm going to find out. . . ." If I couldn't get past two sleepy boys, I'd certainly conceal nothing from their father. Elephants, street fights, and a man who wanted to die . . . Paper or no paper, this was the day I'd have to see a doctor.

8

KNOWING that mine was an apprehensive husband, I planned to say nothing until that evening about my appointment with the doctor, or if birthing the week's edition had been more exhausting than usual, I'd wait until our leisurely coffee klatsch on Thursday morning. But I was disturbed and therefore clumsy, and I trapped myself when Ed telephoned about ten o'clock Wednesday to tell me about the morning's mail.

"I thought you'd like to know there's a letter here from your mother—the postmark is Acapulco."

"She was going to go down for a week or so. . . . Good. I've been wondering when I'd hear from her. I'll pick up the letter this afternoon."

"You're coming to Snoqualmie? How come?"

If I was resolved not to mention the pain in my hip, that was the moment to remember I had to get razor clams out of the locker, or that the electrician in Snoqualmie had called to say our phonograph was repaired. These statements would have been true, but my appointment with the doctor obsessed me and I didn't even think of them.

"I'm going to stop in at the clinic. Funny little pain in my hip. No real reason to go to a doctor, but I haven't had a general checkup for almost two years so I thought I might as well get *that* over with. Just routine . . ."

The pressure of getting out the edition was enough to dull Ed's ear to the hollow ring of this half-truth. "O.K. Good idea . . . What kind of a pain did you say?"

"In my hip. Just a little one . . ."

"Doesn't sound like appendicitis. Well, come into the backshop when you stop to get your mother's letter. If I can break loose I'll take you out for coffee."

Two hours later I limped into the *Record* office, in such a state of mind after what the doctor had told me that I forgot about my mother's letter.

The examination had been thorough. The doctor's painstaking effort to explain what was wrong was meant to be, and should have been, reassuring. Holding the x-ray film against an illuminated glass panel, he traced the outline of the pelvic bone. "And here is the femur, the large thigh bone. It moves in this socket here, the hip joint, and there's a sac, a little sac called a bursa, which acts as a lubricant. . . ." His finger pointed to a spot on the film, irregularly shaped and blurred in outline. "Sometimes there is irritation between these moving parts, and bleeding. A calcium deposit forms, breaks free, and this can cause acute pain. . . ."

And later, after he'd finished his diagnosis: "I think what you need is deep x-ray treatments, which will dissolve the calcium. But I'd like my diagnosis checked by a specialist. I'm going to refer you to a clinic in Seattle."

"Which clinic?"

"The Tumor Institute."

The Tumor Institute . . . To most of the patients there, and to many Seattle people, it is known as the Cancer

Institute. Though the doctor had assured me that my condition was not malignant, I was frightened. Another fear took possession of me: I was going to be less than whole. My unlimited strength was to be limited. My remarkable endurance ("My, how can you get so much done . . .") was to be curtailed.

When the job was hard or the problem was difficult, I had attacked in one of two ways: Either I refused to see how difficult it was, plunged into the middle of it and therefore had no choice but to swim furiously until I reached the opposite shore; or recognizing that I had, indeed, come up against a stone wall, I had simply beat on it until it crumbled. I had never accepted, nor even tried to determine, the limitations of my natural ability; I believed—in fact, the very core of my self-confidence was the belief—that if I stuck with something long enough, and worked hard enough, I would not fail.

When a little child pinches a finger, a mother promises: "I'll blow on it, and make it go away." The doctor was trying to tell me that a complete cure was possible, but in my unreasonable fear of being less than perfectly well (less than remarkable, too) all I could think was that I'd met an obstacle I could not *make* go away. The doctor was talking about rest and heat treatments. No gardening, no hiking, nor any unnecessary exertion. I was to *save* my strength, when the only way I'd ever whipped a problem was to spend it.

With my first taste of panic, I said, "Doctor, I want to take the treatments immediately, and get this over with, and get well."

He smiled sympathetically. "You can begin treatments immediately, of course. But Charlotte, you've got to face the fact that the results may not show for some time. The calcium deposit may dissolve slowly, and then the inflammation of the bursa can be stubborn . . ."

I cut him off. "All right. Three weeks? Four weeks?"

He shook his head. "Three months. Ten months. A year. At least, that's my opinion. We'll let the specialist look at that hip and see what he thinks."

I stood up, and despite myself winced at the sudden, rocketing pain. "When can I go to the Tumor Institute?"

"I'll check with you later, after I've called. Now go home and go to bed."

"Go to bed! At one o'clock in the afternoon? I have things to do!"

"Yes, *go to bed*. And take a hot-water bottle with you."

I went from the doctor's office to the Falls Printing Company, where the venerable newspaper press had been striving to set a new record for Paper Day annoyance. When Ed finished the press run the previous afternoon, it was purring like a tabby cat. When he turned it on in the morning, it snarled once or twice, and stopped. Motor trouble, with the last deadline six hours away.

All electricians were out on jobs, but one of them had left tracks distinct enough to follow. Ed had found him, pleaded with him, and brought him to the shop. When I walked in, the press was repaired and humming, but work was behind schedule and another cog in the Paper Day production line, the newspaper folder, was emitting little cries and grunts in sympathy with the injured press.

Ed called, "Hello, hon" as he ran past on the way to the tool rack. Pliers in hand, he wheeled around and passed me again, on such a fast track that the words "Doc find anything?" were blown out of his mouth.

To his moving back, I answered, "Yes, he did."

Perhaps it was my tone of voice, or perhaps the two brief glimpses he'd had of my face suddenly congealed into a disturbing image. He halted as if he'd reached the edge of a precipice, slowly turned around and walked back. "*What* did he find?"

I stumbled through my recitation. Not sorrowfully but

rebelliously—mad at an aching hip, at a hot-water bottle, at a situation I couldn't bull my way through. "Calcium . . . Inflammation of the bursa . . . x-ray treatments . . . Tumor Institute . . ." Choking, I went through it all. I was a very different person from the woman who for weeks so nobly concealed an aching hip because she didn't want to worry her husband.

Close as I was to hysteria, I observed, and was surprised, by Ed's reaction. I had expected him to be as emotional as I. He always got excited when I cut a finger. He flew into angry panic if I tripped and fell. Now he was calm. His face was ashen, but his hand was strong and steady as he took my arm and led me into his little office.

"Sit down," he said quietly. "I'll take these pliers to Don and I'll be right back." A moment later he was seated across from me.

"Now listen. I don't know what's wrong. I'm going to call the doctor and find out, and tomorrow I'm going to take you to the clinic in Seattle. But I want you to get one thing through your head. *Whatever's* wrong, we can lick it. Our boys have had polio, and now they're well. I had a couple of little heart attacks . . ."

"And shingles!" I sobbed.

"*And* shingles, but that's all behind us. We've been broke, we've been discouraged, and we've been scared, but we came through every time. We will this time."

"I don't *want* to live in a wheelchair!"

His mouth tightened but he said levelly, "Did the doctor mention a wheelchair?"

"He said I couldn't work in the garden, or go for a walk, or do anything . . ."

He took both my hands in his and held them tightly. "If you *did* have to use a wheelchair for a while, then you would. You'd face it, and you'd do it. You were so wonderful when the boys had polio. Whatever it was, you faced it, you didn't even cry. Everyone *admired* you."

He released my hands, placed them in my lap, and stood up. "Here . . ." He lifted the desk blotter and pulled out a thin envelope with a red, white and green border and a row of canceled Mexican stamps. "Read the letter from your mother. I've got a half-hour's work in the backshop and then I'm going to drive you home."

"I came down in the old car. I can't drive home with you."

"Why not?"

Loud and woefully I cried, "Because then one car would be at home and one car down here and how would we get the old car home from the shop!"

"Who cares? Now, blow your nose, and read your mother's letter."

I slit the envelope, and hiccuping softly smoothed out two pages of transparent onionskin, typed single space.

She wrote that she had abandoned the idea of driving up for Christmas. It was short notice, of course, but perhaps I could come down for Thanksgiving? Her new apartment in Mexico City was so lovely, she had such stimulating friends.

The letter was not characteristic of my mother, and for a moment I was afraid that she might not be well. But there was no reference to illness, except that the altitude had "got her down a little," a normal sentiment for someone who lives at 7,400 feet above sea level and knows the golden shores of Acapulco are only a few hours away.

I folded the whispering sheets of onionskin and put them back into the envelope. Only my impractical, dancer-painter-sculptor mother would suggest that I make a 10,000-mile round trip to Mexico City in mid-November. It was our busiest time of year at the shop. As the Christmas holidays approached, it would be a hectic time for me at home, especially since I was trying to finish my new book. She knew all this.

She could not know what the doctor had told me today. She wrote about "a nice visit," and getting to know her "wonderful friends." If I had not been exhausted by my crying spell I would have wept. Mexico City! Avenida Insurgentes! *I* was going to be at the Tumor Institute.

ii

I insisted on driving to Seattle alone. Ed had an important appointment in Snoqualmie, which was the reason I gave; the reason I didn't speak of was that I resented the helplessness which "being driven" to the hospital implied.

"If I can reach Dan by phone, I'll cancel the appointment."

"No! I'm not crippled."

"I have several errands in Seattle anyway."

"Which you had no intention of doing today. No, really, I'd *prefer* to go in alone."

Driving was not as painless as I had insisted it would be, and when I reached the hospital the nearest parking space was two blocks from the entrance to the clinic. I walked up the hill slowly, my right leg throbbing. Each shock of pain reminded me that I need not have been so stubborn about driving in alone. At the door, I paused. When my breathing was even, I opened it and went inside.

The Tumor Institute occupied a section of the basement of the hospital's old wing, where it seemed to be stored, like a key government office which has been moved into an air-raid shelter in great haste.

An unsmiling young woman questioned me, transferring my answers onto a ruled form. When she had finished, I waited expectantly to be directed to the doctor's office.

"You might as well sit down."

"My doctor made an appointment . . ."

She gestured toward the waiting room. "There's a lot ahead of you," she said in a flat, disinterested voice. "Better take a chair, if you can find one."

At long last, "Mrs. Groshell!"

I followed the nurse, but I could not overtake her. She led me, almost at a run, down a corridor cluttered with portable machines, wheelchairs, desks, and here and there a straight-backed chair. Several chairs were occupied by patients, some fully dressed, some in hospital gown and robe. Each silent, lonely person was waiting—waiting for the doctor, for the x-ray technician, for the nurse, or just waiting to be told that there was nothing more to wait for.

"In here. Take off your clothes. Put that robe on." The nurse disappeared.

I faced a row of three-sided booths, the thin wood walls beginning about a foot from the floor. In this cubicle I changed into the cold white hospital garments, folded my clothes, and placed them on the seat.

I pulled back the curtain and looked out. No one in sight. After a few minutes, I pushed the pile of my clothing aside and sat down. The sounds were clearer now. Voices, doors, footsteps, wheelchairs . . .

"Are *you* still in here?" The nurse's forehead was marked by a small, absent-minded frown. She hurried me back to the main corridor, turned right, and continued without pause. Once or twice she looked over her shoulder to make sure I was following.

The examination room was large, sparsely furnished, and cold.

"Wait there." The nurse nodded toward the examination table and was gone.

In thirty-five minutes the nurse reappeared, the doctor following. She was not hurried now. She introduced him formally, and stood by, perfectly calm, perfectly attentive, as he proceeded with the examination.

He was a heavy-set, scowling man, who made it clear immediately that he would never slight a patient, and neither would he waste time. His questions were blunt. When my answer was less concise than he would have been, he frowned; when I replied stumblingly, he ignored my answer and repeated the question verbatim. His fingers were sure as they explored the hip region, and they continued to press relentlessly even when they located the core of pain and I cried out.

He turned to the nurse. "Take her up to x-ray. One on the side, one on the back."

With a nod at me, he walked out.

"This way," the nurse instructed.

I slid to the edge of the examination table and began to turn. A pain caught me so suddenly that I froze.

The nurse's crisp manner dissolved. "Here," she said warmly. "Let me help you down off that perch."

"I can do it."

She smiled sympathetically. "Sure, but why should you?" she said, and virtually lifted me off the table and placed me on my feet.

I followed her to the elevator, and from there to the x-ray room. In ten minutes the nurse and I were retracing the course to the regions below.

"Doctor will see you here."

Once more I waited in the lonely cavern of the examination room, and tried, with an increasing sense of desperation, to concentrate on the games I had invented for my wrist watch.

In an hour the doctor came in. "I have seen the x-rays," he told me. "It is a bursitis. It is not so usual to find this in the hip. More often it is in the shoulder. You should have a series of five treatments, one or two a week. You can make an appointment at the desk . . ."

A nurse I hadn't seen before appeared in the doorway.

"Oh, yes," the doctor said, "yes, I am coming right away."

Between tears and anger I interrupted, "I want to know what I came here to find out! My hip aches. At the moment it aches very badly. You say 'bursitis' but I don't know what that means. I'll take the series of treatments, of course. Then what?"

The doctor's arms dropped to his sides. "I've told you everything I know now."

"But later, after the treatments . . ."

He looked at me levelly. "In time, the calcium should be dissolved. If I said how much time, I would only be guessing."

"But if the pain persists, if there is some disability in my hip . . ."

"That's not our business here. You'd have to go to an orthopedic man."

Like a child, I had believed that if I told this man where it hurt, he would make it go away. Throughout the long, cold morning, I had retained my faith in the absolute cure which was to be mine if I waited long enough, and followed the nurse obediently, and took the treatments and bought the pills.

I began to speak, but he was gone.

iii

When I went to the Tumor Institute for my first treatment, the opening routine was familiar. But when it was my turn, and the door to the black chamber opened, for *me*, my earlier sense of being lost and alone swept through me. The nurse was cheerful, even talkative. With efficiency born of much experience, she moved me into the proper position beneath the great x-ray machine, spread rubber sheets, supported my back with a padded wedge, swiftly measured distances with a steel ruler. In a few seconds the beast's conical proboscis was pointed down to my hip, and she warned me, "Hold *absolutely* still until you hear the bell ring. It's only three minutes."

Instantly, I felt I had to move. My leg, my shoulder, my head—how could I hold them still, when the muscles controlling them were contracting, ready for action? Suddenly I thought—The normal heartbeat is seventy-eight to the minute. If I count seventy-eight pulsebeats three times, the three minutes will be up. . . .

I was still counting when the nurse opened the door, bounced to my side, and exclaimed, "Well, for goodness sakes, you can move *now!*"

I relaxed and smiled at her. The last of the unknowns had been seen and endured. This was a tragic society I had joined, for five brief sessions. But there were only four more, and from that moment on, I would not dread them.

It was a happy Thanksgiving. During the first part of the week the men of my family maintained such marvelous harmony that I caught myself regarding them suspiciously. Ed suggested that Hi focus The Hi-Corner on his reasons to be thankful, and Hi did so without an argument. John lavished a full thirty minutes on his Sports Shorts and voluntarily corrected the spelling. Ed was tolerant, the boys were coöperative; they seemed to be united in bonds of mutual tolerance so strong it amounted to collusion.

The healing peace was disturbed only once, and that was when Ed announced that he and the boys would cook the turkey dinner.

"Oh, no, I'll do it," I protested. "I like to cook, it's my job."

"The doctor said the more you stay off your feet, the better."

"I don't care what the doctor said! I mean, cooking the dinner won't hurt my hip."

Ed persisted quietly. "We've already talked about it. Haven't we, kids?"

Hi and John nodded energetically. It was obvious that they liked their father's plan.

They moved closer to their father, like bodyguards preparing to hurry their charge through a particularly dangerous passage. "*We* are cooking the dinner, Mom," Hi said, and John, giggling at this delightful about-face, added, "See, Mom, three against one."

Our living room contains furniture with more sentimental history than monetary value, but only one item is recognized as mine: It is the yellow chaise longue which Ed gave me when we moved onto a small farm about three weeks after our marriage. Life for a couple farming "for fun" leaves very little time for chaise longues, so my chair had accommodated generations of comfort-loving cats and leisure-seeking Sunday guests before I really sat down in it. Yellow was not its original color (cats and guests had seen to that) and after fifteen Thanksgivings its arms were a little slack and its cushions permanently concave. But it was *mine*, the one furnishing in the house, including the bathtub, that anyone would get out of when I wanted to get in.

After breakfast Thanksgiving morning, the three chefs guided me out of the kitchen, into the living room, and placed me firmly in my yellow chair. Hi covered my legs with an afghan, John brought me a magazine (*Boys' Life*, I think it was, or maybe *Sports Illustrated*), and Ed placed a fresh cup of coffee on the table beside me.

They stood back, the three of them, and viewed me smugly.

"Well, for heaven's sakes, I'm not an invalid."

"Hey, look at Mom," Hi chuckled, "she's getting mad." And Johnny burst into uncontrollable laughter.

"That's enough!" Ed snapped. "Back to K.P., you swabbies." The boys slipped away obediently.

"I'm not really helpless," I protested.

Unnecessarily, and I'm sure quite deliberately, Ed rearranged the afghan and tucked it in carefully at the sides. "I know it," he replied. "You've *never* been helpless. It comes as quite a surprise to me"—and he grinned at me wickedly—"that I kind of like you this way."

It was comfortable in my yellow chair—to think so was in itself an admission, and after a while I also admitted (silently) that it was good to be off my feet. Why had I concealed the ache in my hip until it became too serious to hide? To spare Ed, or to cherish, for my own sake, the feeling of being stronger than a pain? When Ed or the boys had been ill, I had been "brave." "Everyone admired you," Ed had reminded me; wasn't that the secret of my bravery? I could face my husband's illness courageously; recognizing that I might be ill, or weak, or helpless, was quite another thing. The superwoman, I reflected. Always strong, always brave, always admirable. And now a calcium deposit, an angry bursa, had cracked the strength-giving myth. Apprehensive Ed, always nervous at the slightest mishap to me, had taken real trouble calmly; his first chance, I thought guiltily, to be admirable, too. This Thanksgiving morning he'd given thanks because, for the first time, I was just a little bit helpless. Less strong, less brave, less admirable. "And I kind of like you that way . . ." He hadn't been joking.

During preparation of the dinner a few questions were called out to me from the kitchen, most of them concerning the location of a cooking vessel or utensil which (according to them) we either didn't own or I had hidden. I offered to help, at least in an advisory capacity, but they rejected me. For Thanksgiving two or three years earlier, I had purchased a ready-for-the-oven frozen turkey. Until Ed carved the bird, I had contended that the packing company forgot to include the turkey's neck and the giblets—liver, gizzard and heart. But they were there. At the dinner table Ed had found them with the tip of the carving knife, in a sodden, thoroughly cooked plastic bag behind the savory stuffing. The Groshell menfolk had never forgotten the incident—naturally—so whenever I called out from my chaise longue, "Want any help?" one of them replied, "No thanks, Mom, we've already found the giblets."

Late in the afternoon the escort of three surrounded my chair, saluted, and led me to the dinner table. Johnny had set the table with the forks on the right hand side of the plate, Hi had served milk by placing a full bottle of it in the middle of the table like a centerpiece, and there may have been one or two other discrepancies in the formal décor. I noted that their menu didn't include creamed boiled onions or steamed squash, Boston traditions I always honored because I liked them very much, but they had prepared a great deal of everything they liked, so the meal was bountiful.

We sat down, extended both arms, and grasped each other's hands. In this family ring, a silent blessing seemed to pass from one to another. We gave the hands we held a gentle squeeze, released them, and looked up.

Ed said quietly, "We have a lot to be thankful for."

All week I had been thankful for the harmony between the boys and their father. Whether it was real understanding, or merely a Thanksgiving armistice for Mother's sake, the lack of dissension had been like relief from a chronic pain, a pain, I realized for the first time, that had grown enormously. The absence of tension was the first real measure of how tense the struggle between generations had become. I caught Ed's eye and smiled. "Yes, I am thankful, too."

It was a happy meal. We teased each other without bridling. We laughed at jokes we had heard before (or when I told one, at jokes that weren't very funny). We even had one or two serious discussions and terminated them peaceably. Once or twice the boys' approval of their own cooking became so vigorous that Ed glanced at them warningly and said, "Of course this isn't half as good as Mom would have made. . . ." They agreed in unison, with their mouths full.

Ed's face showed how deeply happy he was. Each time a joke was shared, each time an easy ribbing was well taken, his feeling grew. It struck me that for him, as well as for me, harmony in the family had produced a sensation of tremendous relief. I had thought that I was alone in my concern, a solitary guardian of the peace between a man who didn't understand his children and boys who underestimated their father. It wasn't so. If Ed had not been suffering from the same tension, he couldn't be so keenly aware of the lack of it today.

"The boys will do the dishes," Ed pronounced after dinner. I could see that this proposition wouldn't have passed by popular vote, but the boys nodded dutifully.

Hi asked, "Before we start clearing, Dad, can we bring in the—you know. Can we bring them in now?"

The boys fell away from the table and loped to their rooms. They were back in a few seconds, each holding an object behind his back. I couldn't see what Hi was concealing, but John wasn't tall enough to shield the full length of a baseball bat.

"We decided to give you our Christmas presents early," John recited eagerly. "We didn't wrap them, though."

Simultaneously they extended their gifts. From Johnny, a Louisville slugger. From Hi, a first baseman's mitt. Neither had been marked by a ball. They were shiny, resplendently new.

I looked at them and lost the power of speech.

"Well, Mom," Ed chuckled. "All you need now is a baseball."

"I think I've got one," I choked out. "At least, it feels as if I had just swallowed one."

Johnny looked worried. "You're supposed to be happy, Mom, not sad."

"I am happy!"

"We're not going to use them," Hi said, "just in case you think that's why we bought them for you."

"I want you to use them. I wish you would use them . . ."

All three—Ed and the boys—shook their heads. Hi said, "Absolutely not. Never . . ." and almost simultaneously Johnny said, "No, Mom, never. At least, not until after *you* do."

I'd spent most of the day in a chaise longue because the ordinary exertions of standing and walking were so painful. Their gifts to me were two items of major league baseball equipment. A more eloquent statement that I would soon be well couldn't have been made.

I took the bat and the mitt from their hands. "This makes Thanksgiving complete. Thank you, all three of you. It's been a wonderful day."

Ed had known about the boys' plan, but for him, too, it had been a wonderful day, and in its rare closeness to his sons, more wonderful for him than for me. His pleasure in the day reached a crest and he expressed it, impulsively, whole-heartedly, through the one means close at hand.

"Here, kids," he said, reaching into the trouser pocket where he carried bills, "let me pay for the bat and the mitt."

"Gee, no thanks, Dad . . ." Johnny smiled in embarrassment and backed away.

Hi said stiffly, "The presents are from us, Dad. We paid for them."

"I know you did. I'm proud that you did. But they cost a good deal. Let me share the expense. I'll tell you what —here's five bucks."

Hi shook his head. "No, Dad."

Johnny explained quickly, "We don't need the money, Dad. Hi got the mitt for selling subscriptions to the *Times* and he loaned me money for the bat and I gave him some I.O.U.'s. Then, when I deliver papers for him because I'm his substitute, he'll give me some I.O.U.'s back again, whatever I earn."

Ed's joshing smile had faded as Johnny talked. An old sore had been reopened; his face showed his irritation. "Well, use this five for something else, then." With a quick thrust, he stuffed the bill into Hi's shirt pocket.

Hi pulled the money out of the pocket, threw it on the table in front of his father, and walked into the kitchen.

"*Hi!*"

The boy turned and slowly walked back. His body was rigid with refusal.

"This has been a wonderful day," Ed said angrily. "A wonderful day. At this point I'm not going to have you spoil it."

"I was going to start the dishes."

"Good. Just remember what I said."

Hi and John went to work in the kitchen, and Ed followed me into the living room. We talked about many things, other than ourselves and our sons. Slowly, self-consciously, we finished out the wonderful day.

The telephone call from Mexico City came two days after Thanksgiving. My mother was gravely ill. Thanksgiving morning she had helped some friends get settled in a new home. She returned to her apartment at noon in order to prepare a full-course, New England style turkey dinner for three Mexican children. In the evening she drove the children to their home and returned to her apartment. When the woman who shared the apartment let herself in about eleven o'clock at night, she found my mother on the floor beside the living-room sofa. She was unconscious.

"If you want to fly down, I'll help you get ready," Ed promised. "When you decide, let me know."

"I do want to go down."

"You realize, don't you, that you may not get there in time?"

"I know. I want to go anyway."

"All right, fine. I'll call the airlines."

Both my sisters lived in the San Francisco area. If I caught the six o'clock plane, I could spend the night with one of them and the three of us could continue together in the morning.

"You can do it," Ed said positively. He packed for me, drove me to the doctor's office for a smallpox vaccination, and even found the box in the attic where I'd filed away my birth certificate. There were appointments to be canceled, messages to be relayed . . . Ed, who disliked such secretarial chores and abhorred the telephone, took care of it all. As he put me on the plane at six o'clock, he said, "You must remember something, darling. "You're the big sister. You're older than they are, you can take it better than they can. They're going to need you."

"She's not going to live. . . ."

He looked at me squarely. "Mommy, you've just come through a rough experience. I mean, the Tumor Institute. I'll bet the people there could tell you that there are many things worse than dying."

Ten days later, leaving my two sisters, I boarded another early plane, the north-bound morning flight from Mexico City to Los Angeles. My mother's ashes were in my suitcase, and I was carrying her guitar under one arm. Two of her friends had risen at 5:00 A.M. in order to see me off—the American who had recently moved into her apartment, and a young girl who had been a house guest when my mother became ill. I could not check the guitar through with my luggage, for it had no case, and so when the three of us went into the airport coffee shop to wait for plane time, I was carrying it.

We sat down, at a square table, and I placed the guitar in the fourth chair. The waiter, a young man of twenty-five or so, took our orders and returned with them promptly. He arranged the cups, the pots of coffee and hot water, the plate of rolls. This done, he walked around the table to the fourth chair, gently lifted the instrument and embraced it, his fingers in position for playing. He didn't speak. The small, courteous inclination of his head was both a request for permission, and a bow, thanking us for our attention. Softly he began to play.

He was aware of us, because at the end of each song, in the second's pause before the next one, he looked at us and dreamily repeated the polite bow. But when he sang the sweet minor-keyed melodies, he was alone with the guitar. During the first song, another white-coated waiter moved soundlessly across the restaurant to our table. One by one, the other waiters deserted their posts and neither speaking, nor singing, nor by any positive movement or sound intruding their physical presence, they gathered around the boy with the guitar. Fifteen, twenty minutes passed—fortunately, for the management, there were few customers in the café at that hour—and then the waiter stopped singing, respectfully returned the guitar to its chair, and with his last small bow and gentle smile, he turned and walked away. As silently as they had drifted toward us, the others returned to their tables.

Fifteen minutes later I was seated in the plane with the guitar in my lap. As the great airship rose at the end of the runway, I looked back through the little window. There the tiny figures I could imagine to be my mother's friends. There the coffee shop's sun-streaked windows, where a Mexican boy had played her guitar. And in the distance, too far away to see except in my mind, the beautiful and tragic city she had loved. They were out of sight in a moment. Then I hugged the guitar against me, and bent my head over it, and for the first time I wept for my mother.

9

CHRISTMAS HAD PASSED, and New Year's Day. While Ed and I had a tendency to divide the year into quarterly tax periods—thinking fiscally, as it were—Hi and John measured time into intervals between school holidays and dates on which they could expect to receive, or would be expected to give, gifts. By their calendar the first event of the New Year would be Hi's birthday on January 31st.

"It was a pretty important day for me, too," I mused when Ed and I were discussing the impending celebration on a lazy Sunday afternoon. "So very important I resent the fact that it isn't counted as a birthday. It's the nothing day, the aught, the zero."

"A birthday is a record of the past. Now your baby has chalked up fourteen of them, and I'm going to give him an electric razor."

"A what! I can't think of anything he needs less."

"Nor anything he'd want more," Ed replied with a rueful grin.

"Sshhh . . . listen . . ."

The sound that interrupted our conversation had many implications and always sent me running to the backyard. It was the swishing beat of a helicopter blade.

"Maybe Weyerhaeuser's doing some seeding," I said, on my way to the door.

"Not on Sunday."

"Then it's got to be a search of some kind, or a rescue . . ."

It took a few seconds to locate the whirlybird, for slate-colored rain clouds blown by a wintery wind obscured the horizon in the direction from which the sound was coming. The machine emerged suddenly, clopping desperately as she lumbered against the wind.

"It's one of those with two blades. There's a number on it. And it's painted some fluorescent color, sort of yellow . . ."

"Mmm . . ." Ed murmured. "Could be the Coast Guard."

"It's flying toward Mount Si, or around the mountain along the North Fork of the river."

"In either case," Ed replied, "someone is in trouble. . . ."

The Snoqualmie Valley lies among foothills of the Cascades. The range's queenly Mount Rainier is only seventy-five miles to the southwest, but there are few sites in our Valley where the view of the famous 14,000-foot peak is not obstructed by mountains closer to home. Nearest is the 4,000-foot, massive pre-Cascadian mountain everyone in the Snoqualmie Valley owns—Mount Si, named for a lonely homesteader from Ohio whose significant contribution to the pioneer community was to play the fiddle for all-night dances in the back of the general store.

Like all mountains, even mountains with trails, Mount Si offers almost unlimited possibilities for getting lost.

Two or three times a year search parties, helicopters, and three or four branches of government are involved in rescuing hikers who have ignored every rule of common sense and mountain safety. They don't break the code of the experienced mountaineer; they don't even get that far. They disregard, or perhaps feel superior to the simplest rules: Don't go climbing alone. Don't take a short cut. When you climb a mountain, wear shoes and clothing suitable for mountain climbing, and start your hike in plenty of time to return before dark.

Back in August a group of high school girls had left their homes in Seattle on a sunny afternoon, telling their parents they were going to the beach. Instead, they drove thirty miles in the opposite direction to the foot of Mount Si, and just before five o'clock in the afternoon, all but two of them began to climb the mountain.

It is a three-hour hike to the top and coming down can't be accomplished in much less time. The girls, wearing shorts, halters and sandals, reached the summit before dark. On the way down, the failing light was diminished further by the dark forest through which the trail passes. They began to hurry; one of them was sure she could see the trail forty or fifty feet below, so they left the zigzagging path and took a short cut. In ten minutes they were hopelessly lost, and it was growing dark.

By eight o'clock the girls waiting below were frightened. They drove to the U. S. Forest Service ranger station, and reported that their friends were lost. The search began right then and continued all night. By 9:30 the next morning, when the *Record* publisher's wife arrived at the base camp at the foot of the mountain, four groups were combing the slopes and at least half the men had been up all night: The state patrol, the U. S. Forest Service, the King County Sheriff's office, and the Washington State Forestry Department. These men were to receive pay, though not for overtime; a fifth group, which had joined the search about two in the morning, was the Mountain Rescue Council, made up of experienced climbers who work at their own expense, not only buying their own equipment but often suffering the loss of wages at regular jobs they would be attending to if they weren't out on a rescue.

The girls were brought down unharmed. When it got dark, they had sat down where they were standing, crowded against each other for maximum warmth, and waited until light. Then they saw how keen had been their instinct to stop right where they were; they had been huddled, all night, about four feet from the edge of a cliff.

The rescue accomplished, weary members of the Mountain Rescue Council could go back to their jobs, the state patrolmen could get back on the highway, the federal and state forest rangers could return their attention to the prevention of forest fires, and the two deputy sheriffs who had brought a pair of bloodhounds to aid in the search . . .

"Hey!" someone exclaimed as the roll call was completed. "Where's the sheriff's men and the dogs?"

The search for the girls was over, but the search for the sheriff's peerless tracking team was on. The dogs, it was discovered later, had keener noses for the Cub Scouts who had climbed the mountain the week before than they did for the party of girls. Baying magnificently, they dragged the deputies through brush, across rock slides, and along the river, and halted, triumphant and panting, at the crumpled wrappers of a couple of Hershey bars. In due course dogs and deputies, the latter with uniforms torn and eyeglasses broken, were found at the other side of the mountain by the local Ford dealer who happened to be passing that way in a pickup truck.

The mountain-climbing Seattle girls were cold, tired and hungry after their night on Mount Si, their food supply for four having been one package of chewing gum, but they were safe, and the newspaper photographer from Seattle caught several excellent shots of the reunion as the girls ran down the road into the arms of their anxious parents. It was a good story, though no one interviewed the forest rangers, the state patrolmen, the sheriff's deputies or the members of the Mountain Rescue Council.

"Well," said one father, as his daughter was returned to him, "well, we'll just chalk this up to experience." Embracing each other affectionately, they got into a car and drove away.

"*Whose* experience?" I exclaimed to one of the men who had been beating through the mountain underbrush since four o'clock in the morning.

He grinned wryly. "Ours, I guess."

"Did that father thank you, or anyone else?"

He chuckled. "No. I guess he's going to write us a letter."

The helicopter was hovering over one of the nearly vertical gray cliffs on Mount Si's west face. Ed and I were speculating on the purpose of the mission when the telephone rang.

It was an excited *Record* subscriber. "I thought you might want to know about it for the paper. Some boy from Seattle. He's up on the mountain, three thousand feet, at least. He's on a slide and he can't move. The Coast Guard just sent a helicopter. Out at the end of the road past the Norman farm. You know, the one that goes to Ellisville. . . ."

We picked up sweaters, cameras, and my grandfather's opera glasses. "Can we go, too?" Johnny asked.

"You bet you can," Ed replied grimly. "I want both you boys to see what it takes to keep some darn fool from breaking his neck."

A half-mile from our house an offshoot of the county

road turns sharply to the right and runs to the base of the mountain. There, from a patrol officer, we heard the familiar story.

Three youths from Seattle, one of them a University of Washington student, had driven to the Valley early that morning. Mount Si looked like an "easy little mountain" and they decided it would be fun to go up by way of the big rock slide on the west face.

They found it was slow going, and about five hundred feet from the top their progress was blocked by a sheer cliff. They split up, each hunting for the best route to the summit.

Two of the boys moved to the left, the university student to the right. When the shale began to crumble, he had reached a point where any move was impossible. The cliff was tricking him, breaking under his weight; foot and hand holds were much farther apart than he had guessed from below. At both sides were dangerous rock slides. He was trying to decide what to do when the rock he was standing on broke away. He jumped, found a foothold. Now his position was even worse. He was balancing on a small, unstable bit of rock which shifted at the slightest movement. Just below him the precipice dropped away for two hundred and fifty feet. He was trapped, on a rotten rock shelf six inches wide and two inches deep.

He shouted to the other boys, and they went for help. At 1:30 they reached the house at the foot of the mountain where the search parties were now congregating, and one of them telephoned the state patrol.

By two o'clock a veteran mountaineer by the name of Ome Daiber had been picked up by an Air Force helicopter and taxied to the meadow at the foot of Mount Si, and a second helicopter had been dispatched by the Coast Guard. It was Daiber's hope, the patrolman explained, that a 'copter could lower him over the slide so that the boy could be lifted off the cliff. The two other boys were standing beside an emergency car, drinking coffee. I approached them and asked if they had ever climbed Mount Si before.

"No."

"What is your friend wearing?"

"Sport shirt, cotton slacks, loafers. Same as us."

"In January?"

The boys looked away. One of them answered, "Well, it wasn't cold when we started out."

All afternoon we followed the helicopter's futile efforts to rescue the boy. The 'copter made repeated passes, circled, tried again, but the cliff on which the boy was perched so precariously was one face of a ravine too narrow to enter. Darkness, a rising wind, downdrafts, all contributed to the danger.

At length the helicopter dropped Ome Daiber and two other mountaineers on a lower slope, and the men began the ascent on foot. Other mountaineers, summoned by telephone and radio, were arriving by car; two more parties followed the trio headed by Ome Daiber. It was dark by then; the base camp was lighted by the headlamps of trucks and automobiles, and the patrol car spotlights. For two hours those lights shone on the barren rock, while nineteen men climbed the mountain's most dangerous slope to save a thoughtless boy.

"What gets me," one of the spectators commented, "is the helicopter. The one from the Coast Guard, I mean. It's supposed to be ready at all times for rescue at sea. What if some merchant ship or Navy vessel calls for help but it's over here, thirty miles from the Coast?"

"What gets *me*," another man added, "is the cost of the whole thing. Sergeant of the patrol said it would run around $3,000. *If* the helicopter doesn't crash."

"Do you suppose the men who are climbing, Daiber and the others, will get to the kid?"

Frowning, the second man replied, "Guess so. Or die trying."

We overheard many such conversations that night before the rescue was completed. Hi and John heard them, too, and their faces were solemn when we finally left the base camp and drove home. On the following Sunday, just one week later, they saw the same process repeated.

Another University of Washington student, a friend of the boy rescued a week earlier, drove to the same spot. His classmates hadn't made it, but he was sure he could. With three companions he started up the same dangerous slope. They added their own touch to the adventure, however; three of them carried rifles, and the fourth a pistol, for shooting mountain goats.

The outcome was different, too. Three of the boys descended safely, but the leader broke his friend's record. The week before, the rescue was made before ten o'clock at night. This time it continued until ten o'clock the next morning.

Seventy-two persons had been involved in the hunt, among them thirty-two Explorer Scouts who missed a day of school. The Mountain Rescue Council had spent $439 for gasoline and food. Equipment had included three helicopters and an airplane with an estimated value of $1,387,250. The rescuers had forfeited $1,756 in wages. At the supper table Johnny summarized his feelings. "Those Seattle kids," he said, "are sure a bunch of dumb socks."

Later that evening I realized that the subject of a birthday celebration for Hi's fourteenth anniversary had been forgotten during the dinner-table discussion of mountain climbing. I called Hi into the living room. "You said something a few days ago about a birthday party."

"If it's all right to have one," he replied, "could we make it a March of Dimes party?"

"What do you mean?"

"Instead of birthday presents, everyone brings a contribution to the March of Dimes."

"Good idea, Hi," Ed put in quickly. He took my hand and squeezed it hard. On the subject of polio, there was always a small area of pain, a vulnerability we recognized in each other.

"O.K. if I invite ten couples?"

"Couples!" I exclaimed. "You mean, you want to invite girls?"

He smiled self-consciously. "Well gee whiz, why not girls?"

"It's fine. But you've been telling me for some time that you can't stand girls."

"Well, I want to invite girls."

"I remember you did ask girls to the party you had in the first grade."

"Those weren't 'girls,' darling," Ed corrected. "They were simply 'kids.' Up to the fifth grade, all classmates are the same. Kids. At that point an interesting change takes place, and it becomes noticeable that half the kids are boys, and the other half is girls."

Hi said testily, "I don't see what's so funny. You're always telling us not to laugh at people."

"If you think I'm laughing at you," Ed replied, "it's time to change the subject." And I did, quickly, though I noticed that for the rest of the meal Hi and his father talked without looking at each other.

It was a busy week. About noon on Sunday Ed announced that he was going to clean up a few jobs at the office, and I said I'd go with him.

Hi asked, "Want me to come too, Dad?"

Ed shook his head. "No, you were up delivering papers at three o'clock this morning. You ought to take a nap."

"How about me, Dad?"

"No, Johnny. Stay home and take it easy. It's a mean, cold day."

When we returned about four o'clock that afternoon, Johnny was in the kitchen, trying to wiggle out of some of the wettest, muddiest clothes I've ever seen. Hi, he explained, was still up on the mountain.

The meaning of Johnny's simple statement hit Ed like a series of short jabs, each a little harder than the last. "Mount Si?"

"Yes."

More loudly, "You and he?"

"Well, Hi went with Paul, and I went with Roger. We started out together."

Ed's voice was gaining power, like a steam engine picking up speed. "Why did you separate? Why didn't you come down together? Why isn't Hi at home, too?"

Johnny's manner had been sheepish. Now he sounded frightened. "Well, we—that is, me and Roger—wanted to start down because it was raining and we already got pretty wet. Hi and Paul said it had stopped raining and besides they wanted to explore that old mine."

Ed exploded. "An old mine!"

"But they weren't going to stay very long. They're probably back at Paul's house already."

"You phone Paul's house," Ed ordered, "and find out."

No, Paul's mother said, they hadn't returned. But Paul had climbed Mount Si many times, she was sure the boys were all right. An old mine? Paul had been talking about it, but she didn't know they planned to explore it. . . .

In a small, unhappy voice, Johnny transmitted his father's message: If the boys weren't back in thirty minutes, please let us know.

"*Then* what are you going to do?" Johnny asked timorously.

"Call the ranger station and the state patrol."

For twenty-five minutes Ed paced nervously from the living room to the kitchen, and back again. My one or two attempts to soothe him only aggravated his rage and for the last quarter-hour I made stumbling efforts to prepare a meal and didn't speak at all. When the telephone bell rang, I went to answer.

"I'll handle this!" Ed said curtly, taking the receiver from my hand.

It was Hi, calling to say that Paul's mother had a chicken dinner ready and he was invited to stay.

"You be out on the porch in five minutes!" Ed replied. "I'm on my way over to pick you up."

Johnny gathered the courage to ask, "What about his bike, Dad? If he leaves it at Paul's he won't have it for his paper route tomorrow afternoon."

Ed walked out the kitchen door and slammed it behind him.

"He's awfully mad," John whispered.

"I wonder how you'd feel, Johnny, if you'd written a long editorial this week about the stupid, thoughtless kids who get lost on Mount Si?"

"We weren't lost."

"We didn't know that, until Hi called just now."

"But why would Dad act so mad?"

I sighed. It wasn't easy to explain, and harder to justify. "Some people do get mad," I said, "when they are badly frightened."

Perhaps he was afraid of the force of his anger, for Ed did not speak to Hi on the way home. They came into the kitchen, Ed first, Hi behind him, both enveloped in a cold and terrible silence. Without a word, Hi began to take off his boots and jacket, which were even wetter and more heavily caked with mud than were Johnny's. Johnny was watching apprehensively, frozen to the spot on which he'd been standing when his father walked in. It was almost a relief when Ed stopped pacing, turned and faced the three of us, and lost his temper.

"Do you ever read the *Record,* your own newspaper? Did you read the editorial this week? Weren't you at the foot of the mountain last Sunday, and the Sunday before, watching dozens of men risk their lives because some brainless kids got in trouble? We talked about rules of safety in the mountains. We talked and talked and talked. How many did you break today? One. You climbed the mountain on a dark, rainy day, without the proper clothing either for the altitude or the time of year. Two. You left the trail. Three. You didn't stick together. . . ."

Hi broke in, "But Dad, it wasn't raining when we left. The old mine isn't very far off the trail. And besides, Paul and I *did* stick together."

I said quickly, "Paul has been up there a good many times."

Ed frowned at me and turned back to Hi. "You got up at three in the morning," he continued angrily, "and before we went down to the shop I told you to take a nap."

"You didn't tell me. You just suggested it. I didn't think it was an order."

"You didn't think! From start to finish, you didn't think! I could have used your help at the shop, but I figured you were tired. So you climb Mount Si, on a cold, rainy day in January. . . ." Ed stopped, choked on his own words.

I tried once more to ease the situation. "Paul's mother did know where they were going. She gave her permission. I know Hi should have asked us, too, but it isn't as if he . . ."

This attempt, too, was a miserable failure. For a moment Ed looked at me as if I were a stranger he instinctively disliked, and then he addressed Hi. His voice was lower now, but hoarse with feeling. "There'll be no TV for you, Hi. No movies, no privileges of any kind. I can use up your spare time at the shop. Starting next Saturday."

While his father talked, Hi had stripped down to his shorts. His thighs were chapped, his jersey undershorts clung wetly to his body, and there were a few scratches on his face, received—I guessed—from crawling through underbrush. Wet and bare as he was, he stood up straight and looked squarely at his father. "Does that mean no birthday party? I already invited three of the kids."

In his anger, and in my distress over his anger, we'd forgotten Hi's "March of Dimes" party. I caught my breath. What now, I cried inwardly, what now . . .?

For a moment Ed looked at Hi numbly, his face still flushed and paralyzed in its last expression of anger. Gradually the color left his cheeks, the anger fell away, his eyes darkened as numbness left and he felt the pain. "If I said you could have a birthday party, you can have it." He turned abruptly and walked out of the room.

ii

Hi's estimate of "ten couples" had sounded modest. It wasn't until actual preparations began that I realized this fourteenth birthday, if not the full-scale operation of seven years earlier, was far more complicated strategically.

In the first place, the original guest list of twenty (including the host) was not, in Hi's opinion, sufficient unto the day. He had forgotten a certain male classmate, and of course that meant adding the name of one more female classmate. This particular girl's best girl friend might be hurt if she was left out, so Hi had to invite the girl's best girl friend's best boy friend. . . . It was like shortening the legs of a table, in reverse, and Johnny raised a question which helped like a fifth leg. "Am I invited?"

Hi shrugged. "Sure, I guess so, if you'll comb your hair."

It was already obvious that Hi's party was going to take over the house like an occupation army. Johnny had a choice between attending or running away from home.

"Well then, can I invite a couple of *my* friends?"

In Johnny's vocabulary, that meant boys; even when Mitzi took his mind off baseball cards, his philosophy was that it's all right to love girls but you don't have to be friends with them.

"Gee whiz, then there'll be more boys than girls," Hi protested. "I was going to have it balanced."

"In my opinion, ten couples would have assured you of perfect balance."

"Mom, the bigger the party, the more for the March of Dimes."

The menu was another problem, until I ran up a white flag. I had expected to serve cake, ice cream, fruit punch, garnished with funny paper hats and those little crepe-paper rolls we used to call "favors." Hi received this suggestion with a combination of tolerance and embarrassment no face can register more clearly than that of a thirteen (almost fourteen)-year-old boy. "Would you let *me* plan the menu, Mom, *please?*"

"Well, what do you want?"

"Spaghetti and meat balls, and hot dogs. Cake's all right but don't, *please* don't get it decorated with that Happy Birthday Hiram stuff. And no punch, Mom. The kids like real pop in bottles."

The party was something like transferring the field artillery from Fort Lewis to the Yakima firing range. The maneuver was divided into three phases. The first was an afternoon of roller skating at the Y.M.C.A. The second was supper at our house, and Hi issued two directives: No tables were to be "set" and I was to cook twice as much spaghetti as I thought necessary. The third phase was the double feature at the movie house "uptown."

The Y is three miles to the north of our home, and the theater is two miles to the south. Transferring thirty-six boys and girls (plus brother John, who decided to come stag) from house to Y to house to theater to house was accomplished smoothly with the aid of three station wagons, one our own, two driven by mothers who thought we were daft but were willing to coöperate.

During subsequent car lifts Ed was drafted as a bus driver. At supper he was a chow corporal, ladling spaghetti out of three large roasting pans, opening pop bottles, passing the mustard. While the gang was in the theater, he was the janitor, collecting and burning paper plates and napkins, sweeping up cake crumbs, removing smears of tomato sauce from the phonograph, retrieving the hot dog that had rolled under the piano. The invitations he printed for Hi had included a postscript: "My Mom and Dad will take everyone home after the party . . ." and several of the guests lived in those beautiful, inaccessible places which seem so far away at eleven o'clock at night.

At last the party was over. We were all at home, and the boys had gone to bed. The kitchen was clean, the living-and dining-room furniture was in place, the trash had been burned; our house had been returned to us, and the only physical evidences of its occupation by thirty-six eighth graders were the cartons of empty pop bottles in the kitchen and the stack of March of Dimes envelopes on the dining-room table. Ed sat down at the kitchen table and wearily lit a cigarette. "I'll come to bed in a few minutes," he said. "At the moment I couldn't walk that far."

I was leaving the kitchen when Hi came in. He was in his pajamas and he'd been in bed for half an hour, but he was wide-awake.

I thought he might be ill. "Do you want something, Hi? What is it?"

He shook his head. "Nothing. I just wanted to talk to Dad." He walked past me and stood in front of his father. "Dad, I guess I didn't really thank you for the party."

"Yes, you did."

"Well, I mean, I know you probably had other things to do, and it was a lot of work."

"Mom did most of the work. We were both glad to help. We're glad it was such a successful party."

"Oh, boy, it sure was! You should of heard the kids talking about it on the way home."

"Don't think I didn't," Ed replied dryly.

"Yeh, that's right, you were driving. Well..." Hi sighed. "Well, I just wanted to say thanks. I mean, thanks for everything..."

"That's all right, son...."

No reference to the angry scene of the previous week, no apologies, no admission by either of them that this was a reconciliation. But I knew how little they had talked to each other during the week.

"Good night."

They both replied, "Good night, Mom," and both faces turned to me, for an instant, with affectionate, absentminded smiles. They went back to their conversation, and didn't seem to see me leave.

I thought of the night I had tried to help Hi remove his rain-soaked clothes, and Ed had commanded, "Let him do it himself!" Their mutual understanding, so rough-hewn, so gruff, as compared to the way I would have expressed it, had left me on the outside. Once more, a moment of real closeness between them was a moment of rejection for me. It didn't hurt as much as it had before. I felt relieved, not excluded.

I washed and undressed, listening to the murmur of their voices. When I went into the bedroom I turned the knob slowly so there would be no rebuking click as the door closed behind me. That night I slept well for the first time in a week.

iii

There were problems, of course. Though I had finished the novel, my new writing project, a novelette, was going slowly. Theoretically, my hip was improving, but the pain persisted. Though it had been eased by the communion of the birthday party, there was tension between Ed and the boys. . . .

But these realities did not keep me awake. It was the vague uneasiness, the bitter memory, the unfairness or error which could never be corrected, that visited me at night. Again and again I was overwhelmed by a sense of loss, and in the moment of painful insight which sleeplessness sometimes bestows, I knew what I had lost. It was the earlier, happier bond with Ed, worn thin now by the continuing issues over our children. But some nights I wondered if the change had been caused by the children, or was it, as the doctor had so patiently explained to me in describing the nature of bursitis, the natural wearing process that comes with years? We didn't seem to understand each other's roles as mother and father, but wouldn't we be more likely to if we strengthened our understanding of each other as husband and wife?

Such questions were never answered in the lonely darkness of two or three o'clock in the morning, and each day I was a little more tired.

One afternoon shortly after Hi's birthday, my writing had gone so badly that I left it before noon. I was drinking a cup of hot strong tea, when the school bus stopped on the road in front of our house, discharged Hi, and continued on its route.

"How come?" I asked when the boy came into the kitchen. "Half-day of school?"

"They had to send us home early because they had trouble with the furnace."

"Where's Johnny?"

"He took the bus to Snoqualmie. He's at the bowling alley."

"No furnace trouble at the bowling alley, eh."

"Guess not," Hi said absently. "Mom, could I talk to you, confidentially?"

The question warmed me. "Of course."

"I thought, since this is something you'd know about, you might give me some advice about—about how to get along with a girl."

"The girl you invited to your birthday party?"

"No, another one. She didn't come to the party."

"Oh, she didn't."

"You don't even know her. She's new."

I thought to myself—I'll say she is—but I could see that my term as adviser would end abruptly at the first hint of facetiousness. And I wanted to keep the job, I wanted it badly. I was touched and reassured by his asking to talk to me confidentially on any score, however small a part of his total growing up it might represent. Briefly, perhaps, but voluntarily, he was coming to me.

"You said 'get along' with a girl. Do you mean this is a girl you like and you want her to like you?"

He nodded. "That's the general idea."

Once before he had asked for the same kind of advice, the only previous case of "liking" a girl, as far as I knew.

I hadn't been very helpful. I had advised him to "act natural." This was impossible. He could run backwards to field a Texas Leaguer and shoot it to second for a quick out, but in the girl's presence he tripped over his own feet. I had told him to remember his manners, but this, too, had proved an impractical bit of counsel.

When I drove them to the movies, Hi opened the back door of the car and stood aside. She gave him a blank look, flung open the front door and leaped into the front seat next to me. My final suggestion, and the one which killed the romance, was to "play hard to get." Up to that time, the girl had accepted a few invitations and during the school picnic she let him push the swing in which she was seated. But when Hi pretended he couldn't see her, she did the same, only in her case it hadn't been an act.

Remembering this earlier failure, I began bravely, "Well, always act natural."

"*She* sure doesn't."

"That," I said with conviction, "is a very good sign. . . ."

As we talked, I thought many times how much I was enjoying myself. "You know about girls, Mom . . ." he admitted willingly; how I cherished that scrap of evidence that this growing, changing, rebellious boy, with the uncertain voice and the electric razor, still needed me.

We were sitting at the kitchen table when Ed came home. He was in good spirits. "I was just talking with your principal, Hi. He told me the school had to close while the furnace is repaired. Come on, I'll take you out and buy you a hamburger. Then Mom won't have to interrupt her writing."

I said quickly, "I've stopped writing for the day. I'll make lunch for the three of us." What was the matter with me? Even to my own ear, my voice sounded high and sharp. I, who begged for freedom to write, didn't want to write at all. I loved time to myself, but I was

trying to keep them from going off without me. . . .
"There's some spaghetti left from the birthday party."

Ed laughed. "Amazing . . . Say, Hi, your principal told
me you're top salesman in your class."

Hi had told me that the school's annual magazine subscription campaign was underway.

"Top salesman, eh?" Hi had not mentioned this achievement, and I was surprised, for each student's sales were
rewarded with "credits" and the best salesman in any
class received a radio or prize of equal value.

Ed asked the pertinent question. "You're going to be
getting a pretty nice prize. Why haven't you told us anything about it?"

Color rushed to Hi's face. My son, blushing! I looked at
him incredulously, and then what knowledge I had of
the campaign's "credit" system fused with whatever in-
tuition I had about the mind of a fourteen-year-old boy
and I knew what had happened. He had transferred his
"credits" to the girl's account. She would get the prize.

He didn't answer. Ed looked at him curiously, and then
grinned. Either the principal had revealed Hi's secret or
Ed didn't want to make an issue over the unanswered
question. "Magazine subscriptions," he said good-naturedly. "I thought the *Seattle Times* didn't allow its
independent dealers to sell other publications."

"What's the use of telling you!" Hi burst out. "You
wouldn't understand!" Tears in his eyes, he turned and
fled.

We'd had so many scenes in the past few months our
reactions had become formalized. Ed was always puzzled,
then irritated, then angry—very angry at Hi or John, a
little angry at me because he sensed I was taking their
part. I was always one person suddenly wrenched in two,
the mother comforting her sons, the wife supporting her
husband. Now, for the first time, our feelings were identical; Ed and I were united in helplessness.

"Have some tea," I said foolishly.

Ed whispered, "For crying out loud, what was that about?"

"You wouldn't . . . No, I mean, *we* wouldn't, understand."

Ed looked at me thoughtfully. "Did you sleep well last night?"

"Not very."

"You look awfully tired. Why don't you knock off writing for a few days?"

"Not write!" I swallowed hard. I was about to prove I wasn't too tired to write by bursting into tears. "You *know* I feel terrible when I'm not writing. How could you suggest . . . ?"

Ed picked up his teacup and looked in it. "I guess you're right," he said wearily. "I guess I wouldn't understand."

10

THE PUBLISHERS of large metropolitan dailies, like the czars of big business, keep a comfortable distance between themselves and their customers; when they affirm that what's good for the newspaper is good for its subscribers, the voices raised in contradiction are seldom heard on the top floor. For the owners of nine thousand weekly newspapers, there are no bulletproof limousines or private elevators. They don't look down on their readers, benevolently or otherwise; they live with them. Some want a certain story to appear in the paper, others will be gunning for the editor if it does. Fifty-two times a year the owner of the "Blab" tries conscientiously to include everything he ought to print and to omit every story he shouldn't, knowing perfectly well that local opinion may differ strenuously as to which is which, and probably at his expense.

There have been times when the *Snoqualmie Valley Record's* publisher had a moral, if not a legal right to

print the awful truth. For example, a prominent businessman, who was an active community leader and a respected
member of his church, asked Ed to reprint the front page
of an old edition of the *Record*, just as it had been published originally except for one news story.

Ed located the page in the bound file.

"That story," the man pointed out. "There, where it
says I was a partner in a new business."

"But you were, weren't you?" Ed asked. "As I recall,
I wrote that story after talking to you personally."

"But couldn't you change it a little, just say I was 'interested' in a new business, or something like that, or else
leave my name out altogether. Yes, that would be best.
Just leave me out of it."

"I don't get it . . ." but as he spoke, he did. The enterprise in question had gone into bankruptcy. As a partner,
this man was in danger of losing other profitable holdings.

Ed closed the bound file. "In the first place, it wouldn't
work. If you tried to offer a phony page of the *Record* as
evidence, your partner would have no difficulty at all
digging up an authentic copy of the same edition. In the
second place, I've had a few disagreements with people
around here—sometimes I was wrong, sometimes they
were. I've been called a few names I didn't deserve. But
in all my years in the Valley no one has thought so little
of me as to make the suggestion you've just made.

"And in the third place, you've just given me a news
item for this week's paper. I'm going to report this conversation accurately, word for word, every word true. Be
sure and keep the front page this time. Then you won't
have to come to me in a couple of years and ask me to
reprint it."

For a few weeks a certain awkwardness characterized
the businessman's relationship to the *Record*, but of
course no such news item was written. Our job, as Ed

saw it, was to build, not to destroy, even if that meant telling less than the full truth about some of our citizens.

Once the mother of an errant young man brought me a news item she had written herself concerning her son's unsuccessful attempt to steal a case of beer, and his subsequent arrest and conviction. She was astonished when I didn't accept it.

"We don't publish stories about such minor offenses," I said.

"Minor!" she exclaimed. "They had it in the Seattle papers!"

She was nettled at the *Record's* conservatism, but she left the office quietly. Another reader was harder to convince.

She was a plump, friendly young lady, best known in a town of 1,000 for the fact that at twenty she had received an advance degree from one of Washington's largest hospitals for the insane. She was "cured," in that aside from her persistent friendliness there was little noticeable difference between her behavior and that of the rest of us.

Perhaps a "bad spell" had been brewing for some time, or perhaps the patched-up structure of her sanity collapsed suddenly at five o'clock in the morning. In any case, that was the hour at which she left her home and proceeded across town to get her picture taken.

The photographer she selected was our printer, Bob. For some time before he applied for a job at the *Record*, Bob had been known as "that young fellow who takes pictures."

Jeptha was born to be buxom, and had apparently maintained her sanity for as long as she had by eating a great deal; God's gifts had been substantially increased by chocolate sundaes, French fries, and so forth. She must have been an impressive figure as she strode out of her house, barefoot, in pajamas, and hellbent for having her picture taken. Apparently she had been concealing a fuming hatred for all the local merchants; as she progressed, she beat with her fists on the glass doors and windows along the way, leaving, at each furious pause, some broken glass and a portion of her pajamas. Snoqualmie residents are sound sleepers. The first to see Jeptha was Bob, and he did so under protest.

She marched up the walk and onto his front porch. Pummeling the door with both fists, she shouted, "Come on out and take my picture! Come out and take my picture!"

Sleepy and confused, Bob stumbled to the front door. When he opened it, two-hundred-pound Jeptha was dancing on his front lawn. The last shred of her pajamas had been lost somewhere along the route. In smashing windows, she had cut herself; the tremendous area of pink-and-white skin which Jeptha, unclothed, offered to view, was striped and daubed with blood from her injured hands. "Take my picture!" she caroled, pirouetting toward the door.

But before Bob closed the door and phoned the town marshal, he didn't forget his manners. "Sorry," he said politely to the naked, gaily laughing young lady, "I wasn't expecting you."

The *Record* carried no report of Jeptha's exploit, although it was widely discussed all week. "I wouldn't give much for the picture she wanted Bob to take," one of our readers remarked, "but I sure wish someone had been taking movies while the town marshal was stuffing her into the prowler car."

No other *Record* subscriber equaled Jeptha's dramatic bid for the front page. Unquestionably there were others who were no better than they should be, but the local sinners didn't expect to see all their activities faithfully reported in the local newspaper and even when we knew better our editorial policy reflected our conviction that Snoqualmie Valley residents are kind and true.

Some doubt was cast by a young man who asked for $400 because he had been mentioned in a magazine article about the *Record*. However, we didn't know him personally. He was a *cheechaco*, or newcomer, not a *real* Valleyite. Briefly we entertained the whimsical notion of telling the truth, and nothing but the truth, in a news item, but of course we didn't. The magazine dismissed his demand and shortly thereafter he moved away. For the first and last time, his name did appear in the newspaper—in a short piece noting his departure.

Years had passed since the incident and I had forgotten the name of the money-hungry *Record* reader when another subscriber voiced the same sort of demand. Because his name had appeared in one of my books, he thought he should receive a share of the royalties.

The conversation took place in Ed's office on a cold, gray afternoon after I had muddled my way through a particularly dream-harried and sleepless night. Hi was still smarting over our lack of "understanding" and Johnny had been reminding me daily that he still wanted to work in a grocery store, and hadn't I promised to talk to Dad about it? I knew how to handle the man's request and did so in a reasonably low, controlled tone of voice, but I was anything but calm when I told Ed about it afterward.

"You shouldn't be so upset," Ed told me. "Remember that other fellow, five, six years ago?"

"Yes, but this one has such a nice wife, and nice kids . . ."

"Maybe they don't understand him," Ed said wryly.

"He's well known, active in clubs, a steady worker. In other words, a typical good citizen . . ."

"Look, one of our prominent businessmen wanted me to fake a page of the paper. He wasn't typical of our local merchants and the man you talked to this afternoon isn't a 'typical' husband and father."

"But it was blackmail!"

Ed shrugged. "Of a kind, yes. But it was a ridiculous demand. You sent him packing, that's the end of it. Forget it."

"I feel so—so disillusioned, I guess you'd call it."

Ed grinned. "You mean, one of our subscribers is a stinker? My dear girl, when were you born? He's not a bad guy, but he thinks he smells money. To tell you the truth, I hope he's got a good nose for it. Maybe we won't have to float another loan."

"It isn't funny!"

Ed looked at me closely. "Why isn't it? A year ago, even a few months ago, you would have laughed it off, or at least you would have tried to. What's happened to your sense of humor?"

"I don't know. I feel like an old rubber band that's been stretched so often and so hard it doesn't snap back."

"You're tired. Come on, we'll go home."

Some months earlier I would have resisted, but I went along willingly. We drove home through a cold, driving rain. Shivering, I walked from the car into the kitchen. The mechanics of removing my dripping raincoat and placing it on a coat hanger seemed almost too difficult to master. I gave up and dropped the coat on a kitchen chair. Then I stood in the middle of the kitchen, looking around helplessly in an equally exhausting effort to imagine how I would cook dinner.

"I think I'd better go to bed," I said suddenly, "if you and the boys . . ."

"We'll take care of ourselves, don't worry. Please go right to bed."

I walked into the bedroom, undressed, got into bed and drew the bedclothes up around my ears. I was still shivering. I felt miserable, ill, cold beyond all warming, and alone.

The bedroom door opened quietly. It was Ed, with my basset hound Jo in his arms.

Germ-conscious, fastidious as he was, as rigid as were his rules about dogs getting on sofas or entering the dining room during meals, Ed pulled back the bedclothes and lowered Jo onto the bed beside me. Then he replaced the covers, carefully tucked us both in, and without a word, walked out and closed the door. With my warm, round dog pressed against me, and a long, soft basset hound ear against my cheek on the pillow, I closed my eyes and slept.

ii

"What you need," Ed decided at breakfast, "is a change of scenery. Let's take a trip."

"We can't."

Ed grinned. "Well, no, we can't. We happen to be in between Linotype operators. Also, our bank balance is low. Have you got any other reasons?"

"No."

"In that case," said the optimist I married, "we'll go."

I would have argued longer, and perhaps successfully, if the mail that afternoon had not contained a surprise. It was a notice that our "due bill" with a certain airline had to be cashed by March 25 or the credit would be canceled.

The due bill is a cherished tradition of country publishing. It is actually a credit, extended in most cases by hotels, in exchange for advertising of equal value in the newspaper. An agency is the go-between and charges the editor (not the hotel) fifteen percent for making the arrangements, but a hundred dollars' worth of space in the newspaper can buy eighty-five dollars worth of lodging and thus the due bill has inspired many a holiday, especially in the plush days when the credit could be used for meals as well as rooms.

It has also solved the problem of what to do with relatives who are dependent and eccentric, or just penniless and unbearable; one publisher whose aged uncle was a little odd, put the gentleman up in a nice hotel for eleven years. The readers of his newspaper may have wondered why every edition of the paper contained a large advertisement for a certain hotel in a city two hundred miles away, but Uncle enjoyed the metropolitan life and the editor bought peace at home for fifteen cents on the dollar.

A due bill from an airline is unusual. When it was offered we signed up gladly, confident that in a year's time we'd have to make business trips which would use up our credit. But the one year in which going someplace could be done free, or practically so, we had no reason to go any place and many reasons for staying home, and now, the airline notified us, the contract would expire in ten days.

"All right, we will take a trip," I agreed when Ed showed me the notice. "When I go to Seattle tomorrow, I'll make the reservations."

"This line doesn't have a big territory," he pointed out. "Washington, Oregon, part of Idaho. If the two of us try to use up $182.50 worth of credit in two or three days, we're going to be flying around in circles."

"Then we'll all go. The four of us."

"Take the kids out of school?"

"You bet," I said. "It will be a good lesson in geography."

Ed said dryly, "It sounds to me more like a lesson in arithmetic."

The clerk at the airline ticket office was both efficient and courteous. "Oh, yes," he said when I presented our credit card, "we're happy to serve you. Where did you want to go?"

This was a point we hadn't discussed at home. "Well," I said thoughtfully, "what have you got?"

"I beg your pardon?"

"Where do your planes go?"

He looked at me strangely but controlled himself and smiled politely. "Here is a map showing our routes."

I studied the map and the cost chart at the back of the folder.

"May I help you?" he asked. "That is, if I knew your destination . . ."

"I want to go to Boise, Idaho, or Medford, Oregon."

Boise is in one direction, Medford in another. There is no imaginable circumstance which would make these two cities interchangeable on anyone's itinerary.

"You mean Boise *and* Medford."

I shook my head firmly. "No, Boise *or* Medford."

The flight to Boise would have cost more than $182.50. The flight to Medford cost less than $182.50. "I know what we'll do," I decided at last. "We'll go to Medford, but we'll wait until Friday morning instead of taking the family plan on Thursday."

"Then you'll have to pay full fare for yourself! It increases the cost of the trip!"

"I know," I said happily. "Will you fix up the tickets, please."

The following Friday we checked in for the southbound milk run. Hi and John had flown only once before. "Flying is monotonous," I had assured them whenever they sounded as if they were underprivileged. "The only ex-

citing part is taking off and landing." By that definition
the local plane from Seattle to Medford offered unparal-
leled excitement, for it made a stop every fifty to seventy-
five miles.

"We don't ever get very far up, do we, Mom?" Johnny
commented after two or three take-offs.

The first night we slept in a motel in Medford, and the
second night, on the return trip, we took rooms in a Portland hotel. In both cities we rented cars and ate in good
restaurants.

"It was a wonderful trip," I said when we got home
Sunday night. "A real rest. But I have a hunch that even
with a due bill for the plane it wasn't exactly free."

Ed chuckled. "No, it wasn't. As a matter of fact, I'm
glad I haven't totted up what we spent in order to 'save'
$182.50."

"Don't."

He put one arm around me and drew me down into
the chair. "I won't. You can't know how relieved I am to
see you more relaxed. That's what counts with me."

"The boys enjoyed it, too. Johnny took his entire collection of baseball cards and Hi took his electric razor."

"Then," Ed murmured, rubbing my cheek, "it was a
good trip, for all four of us."

11

THE THREE-DAY HOLIDAY was beneficial in several ways. As Ed noticed, I was more relaxed. More and more I had been meeting the smallest domestic crisis either by coming up swinging or bursting into tears. I was still earning the cherished "My goodness, how do you get so much done!" I could write a book, make a speech, instruct a new reporter, or appear on a television show. But let the milkman leave three quarts instead of four and I fell apart. The change of scenery, brief as it was, refreshed and steadied me.

It did something for the rest of us, too, by supplying a project, so rare these days, in which we were happily united. Just a trip and a short one at that; recreation, "fun," a weak substitute for working together as we once had done; but a family venture, nevertheless, and one in which there was virtually no opportunity to disagree.

"I can't stand these fathers who say, 'I want to be a pal to you, son,'" Ed remarked with a grin, "but over the week end I felt I was, and I liked it."

We all began the week with new resolutions, or so it seemed to me because I was so ennobled by my own. I was to finish the novelette, instead of brooding over this or that passage and becoming more and more frustrated as I rewrote it, burned it, and wrote it again. Subscribers who thought their news items should have been on page one, milkmen who didn't leave enough milk, even a friend who wanted money because I mentioned him in a book—they would all find me calm and philosophical, and as a mother and a wife, I would be more understanding. . . .

It was a good role I chose for myself, and I was able to play it for almost a week.

Two incidents, neither important on the surface, tore away the curtain which had been concealing the other actors and revealed that the conflict between my husband and my sons, and the tension between Ed and me, were as lively as ever. If the struggle was quieter, so quiet I could deceive myself into believing it had ceased, it was also deeper.

The first episode grew out of the old question: what should we print in the *Record*?

A high school boy whose parents had been vociferous in criticizing one of our superintendents of schools took things into his own hands and gave the superintendent a beating severe enough to break his jaw. The man was hospitalized; there were undoubtedly very few people in his school district who didn't know about it; but his wife telephoned and requested that nothing appear in the paper. It was her feeling, and her husband's, that the printed reminder of a news story would keep the issue alive much longer than otherwise and would therefore worsen a situation already difficult for everyone. Ed agreed, and no report of the boy's attack on the superintendent appeared either in the *Snoqualmie Valley Record* or the *North Bend Record*.

The day after that week's editions were printed and

mailed, a young man majoring in journalism at the University of Washington visited the *Record*. He was preparing a term paper on weekly newspapers; after an afternoon in our shop, Ed invited him to dinner. He was a tall, earnest boy, with a deep voice and a way of asking questions in rapid succession and then leaning toward the speaker as he listened critically to every word. Hi and John admired him immediately, for being bigger and older, and in a position not only to question their father but to disagree with him.

At the dinner table Ed referred to the high school boy's assault on the superintendent as an example of the kind of incident he felt should not be covered by a small-town newspaper.

The college student looked at him quizzically. "Isn't that suppression of news?"

"Yes, of course it is."

"But as the voice of the community, isn't it your responsibility to print the truth?"

Ed replied dryly, "You mean, fearlessly."

The boy nodded. "Yes, I do. From what you've said, I gather that your reason for not printing a story was less editorial policy than it was the fact that the superintendent *asked* you not to print it."

"In this particular case, that may be so. I didn't know the ins and outs of the situation, and didn't have time before the paper came out to look into them. But I did know the superintendent, and he is an honest man. He must have had good reason to ask me not to print a story, so I respected his request."

"But that's not *policy*. That was entirely personal."

Ed smiled. "Life in a small town is very personal. Almost every decision the publisher of a Cow Corners Gazette makes is personal, in the sense that it involves someone he knows, or someone who is directly affected by someone he knows."

"That superintendent would never have asked the Seattle dailies to leave out a legitimate news story."

"Of course not. But the *Record* is the paper that stays on the living-room table all week. It contains news about the grade schools and high schools right here in the Valley. It isn't just the adults who read it—the kids do, too. I have left out many news items which I knew would appear, or even had already appeared, in the Seattle papers."

The journalism major shook his head disapprovingly. "It's not my idea of the way to edit a newspaper."

"It wasn't mine, when I was an editor in Chicago. But let me ask you this—have you ever lived in a small town?"

"No. But surely the principles of good journalism are not governed by the size of the population. For instance, didn't you tell me the *Record* used to carry reports of cases heard in the local police court?"

Ed nodded. "That was before my time. One of the *Record's* former publishers did run a list of arrests and convictions. Mostly traffic violations."

"Wouldn't you say that showed integrity?"

Ed smiled. "Not particularly. That feature was discontinued because whenever the week's report contained the name of someone in a position to buy a lot of printing or advertising, the editor with 'integrity,' as you call it, omitted that name. The police judge and the clerk felt it wasn't fair to publish names of all the poor, unimportant little guys who got hauled in, and omit the name of a prominent citizen who had been driving while drunk. Print them all, or 'suppress' them all, that's what they believed. The editor wouldn't, so they refused to give him the list."

The boy said, "Well, I feel strongly that all news should be reported. The trouble with journalism today is that the policy makers are practical men. They have forgotten about ideals."

"I have ideals," Ed said quietly, "but I wouldn't have much respect for them if they were harmful to other people."

John had been restless during this discussion, but Hi had listened attentively, and after our dinner guest left Hi faced his father in a way I had begun to think of as his let's-fight-and-settle-it expression. "Dad, what did you think of that fellow?"

Ed gestured toward the departing automobile. "That college boy?"

Hi's mouth stiffened. "Well, you don't have to call him a *boy*, I mean in that tone of voice. Personally, I liked him a lot."

I could see that Ed was determined to handle this lightly. "So did I, Hi, so did I. I wasn't trying to sound superior when I called him a boy. That's what he is, to a man fifty years old. He's full of theory, of course. He should be, at his age. And I'm afraid growing up is going to be a slow process for him as long as he is more interested in asking questions than he is in hearing answers."

"He listened to everything you said."

"*Listened,* but didn't hear."

Hi said stubbornly, "Well, wasn't he right? I mean about keeping a story out of the paper?"

"In editing a newspaper, Right and Wrong isn't that clear-cut. It's a matter of judgment. You can have a general idea of what should be published and what shouldn't, but in a way you have to make an independent decision for every story. In the case of the beating given the superintendent, you know what my decision was."

"Yes, but were you *right?*"

Ed looked at his straining, quarrelsome fourteen-year-old son and said wearily, "Hi, if you were really interested in the *Record,* I'd sit down with you and argue about this all night. But you've made it pretty plain that you are not really concerned about our newspaper, so if you don't mind, I'd like to drop the subject. It's time for the ten o'clock news."

I put in quickly, "Hi, John, bedtime . . ."

Hi ignored this interruption. "What's that got to do with it, whether I am 'concerned,' as you say, or whether maybe I'd like to do something different from what you do, going down to the shop practically every day of the week, grind, grind, grind."

Ed slammed a fist onto the table. "Damn it, that's enough!"

"I just want to talk things over. . . ."

Ed shook his head angrily. "No, you don't. You want to prove something. Most of all, you want to prove I'm wrong."

I walked between them and turned on the television set. The genial voice of the announcer broke into the argument, and reassured me, as my husband walked off in one direction and my son in the other, that a certain stomach alkalizer would take care of everything.

The discussion ended there, but it had dissipated the rosy mist in which I'd been living since the week end. I slept poorly and rose in the morning with an aching sense of hopelessness. My work went badly both that day and the next. Calm, philosophical, understanding . . . How egotistical my resolutions were. What a foolish ostrich I'd been.

There was no overt act, no visible proof, but the tension seemed to increase every day. On Saturday morning I had to relinquish my last bit of hope that no trouble was abuilding except in my tired, anxious mind.

Ed brought me the morning's mail and then went back to the shop. There was nothing to upset me in the first three letters. A woman in Dublin, Eire, wrote that she had read one of my books, her husband had deserted her and her five children, and she wondered if readers of our newspaper would be kind enough to send her their cast-off clothing. A second letter reminded me that my club dues were payable the first of the month; and a third, attached to a twenty-page manuscript, asked me to read the enclosed story and tell the writer where to get it published. It was the next letter which struck me a hard blow. A note from a magazine editor, describing my last manuscript as "tired writing" and adding, I suppose to console me, that "everyone turns out poor stuff occasionally."

I meant to pour a cup of coffee and drawing on its reassurance, read the note again, more carefully. But my hand was unsteady and I dropped the cup. It fell to the floor, broke into a dozen pieces, and splashed scalding liquid on my feet. I dropped into a chair, trembling.

The boys heard the clatter of the breaking cup and ran into the kitchen. "What happened, Mom? Something bad in the mail?"

I shrugged. "Not good."

"A rejection slip?" Hi asked sympathetically. That was a term they had teethed on.

"Not exactly, but it amounts to the same thing." I read them the disturbing letter.

They sat down across from me. Instinct told me—"This is it. It's been coming for days, and here it is. . . ."

Hi asked, "Is it O.K. to talk to you about something?"

"Certainly."

"You're feeling all right?" Johnny asked with a little worried frown.

"Of course!" I tried to say calmly.

Flustered, Johnny said, "Gee, well then why . . . ?"

"Mom," Hi began firmly, "the thing is, when are we going to settle anything?"

"Settle what?" I asked defensively.

"The different things we talked to you and Dad about, or especially to you. And you always said, wait a little while."

At that point I knew, or at least, sensed, what they were going to say. I could not anticipate the exact questions, but the issues, hovering in the distance for so long, were beginning to collect into definite shapes.

Fatalistically, I beckoned to the storm. "Would you give me a specific example, Hi?"

"Remember how you were going to talk to Dad about selling the shop?"

"I said that *sometime* I would tell him what you and Johnny had said to me."

Hi persisted, "Well, did you tell him?"

I shook my head. "No. I wasn't sure that you wouldn't change your minds. In any case, the man from California has undoubtedly bought another plant by now."

"But there's other things, too, Mom," Johnny put in. "Gee whiz, it was way before Thanksgiving I asked about getting a job in a grocery store. Now it's almost Easter."

"You got another job, didn't you? I mean, as Hi's substitute on the paper route."

"*That's* not enough, Mom. That's really *his* job, not mine."

"You wanted money for Christmas presents, wasn't that it? That's past. There's no point in making an issue of it now, is there? And I have an idea you're too young to work in a grocery, anyway."

"All right, some other place!" Johnny exclaimed. "You still didn't answer the question."

"Johnny, do you feel I've kept you from talking to Dad about getting a job?"

Johnny looked uncomfortable. "No, not exactly. I admit, I didn't keep asking you. But you sort of kept me from asking, too. I mean, I knew you didn't want me to talk about it."

"Same about my column, Mom," Hi said. "I talked to you a long time ago about when I could stop writing The Hi-Corner every week."

"And I told you, it's the most popular feature in the paper. It's important to the paper. . . ." I broke off. Even the outer appearance of being calm was vanishing too quickly. "I'm sorry, kids," I said, "I am tired this morning and I have to go out to my writing house and finish an article. I was supposed to mail it yesterday. Let's talk later today, O.K.?"

"It's Saturday," Johnny reminded me. "You don't write on Saturdays."

"I have to today," I replied, truthfully. "Two women at the shop are going to be off Monday so I'll be down there all day. That's why I want to finish my writing today."

Hi stood up as I did. "Maybe I shouldn't ask you this, but isn't it true, Mom, that working at the *Record* makes it harder for you to do your own writing?"

"It takes some time," I said, defensive once more. "But it isn't often that I go to the shop in the morning, too."

"Why do you go to the shop at all?"

"Go to the shop at all . . ." I repeated. "Hi, you *know* why."

Because we had always worked at the shop, together. Because the *Record* was our family enterprise, our binding, unifying, strengthening partnership . . . no, I thought unhappily, be honest. That's changed. The partnership has split in two, whether we see it or not—and curiously enough, the boys are willing to admit it. It's the sentimental, let's-keep-it-that-way parents who cannot. Why do

I go to the shop at all? Because my husband is already suffering from the loss he can't admit, because the four-way family partnership *is* gone, and I am beginning to see that I must replace it with something much stronger, much closer, between the two of us. Because I cannot let him feel deserted entirely . . .

"Is it such a crazy question to ask?" Hi insisted huskily. "I don't care what you say, we know it's hard for you to do your writing and work there, too, even if it's only for a few hours a day. Why don't you concentrate on your writing and let Dad concentrate on his job?"

"But it isn't *his* job," I cried out, "it's *ours*."

"It seems to me," Johnny said matter-of-factly, "that your writing is like a job of your own. Like I want to work in a grocery store and Hi has his paper route."

I said helplessly, "Well, maybe it is, though I've never thought of it that way."

"Everyone," Johnny said flatly, "feels like having something of their own."

"You don't understand. . . ." We've reached a plateau, I thought distractedly. It's been Father and Mother who didn't understand them. Now they don't understand *us*. . . . Where is the wisdom to come from? From which side will the hands be extended to draw together the widening gap?

"I think that if the newspaper really means something to Dad," Hi said carefully, "it wouldn't have to be ours, the way you keep saying. He'd like to have it *his*."

"Please," I burst out, "let's talk later. . . ."

They looked at me dumbly, their faces suffused with doubt, affection, resentment, and a half dozen other emotions involved in not knowing what's got into Mother.

"Sorry, Mom," Johnny mumbled.

"Didn't mean to upset you," Hi said, and the two of them withdrew, unsatisfied, thwarted, their appeal turned down. Nothing was "settled." At my age, I had learned nothing ever is, but at twelve and fourteen, the problem must be, and it grows, and spreads, and eats into you, until it is.

It was just a quarter to six when the telephone rang. The sound caught the three of us—Hi, John, myself—in pursuits typical of a family which expects Father to come home for dinner in ten minutes. Hi had finished his paper route and was hurrying into dry clothes. John was seated at the living-room table, working industriously to finish the project which had employed him all afternoon; he had been clipping and filling out every coupon in the back pages of a magazine. And I was standing near the refrigerator, looking moodily at yesterday's lamb roast and wondering whether a clever wife spends this last ten minutes in the kitchen starting dinner, or in her dressing room, combing her hair.

"I'll get it!" I called absently and lifted the receiver.

It was Ed's voice, but with a formal overtone indicating that someone he scarcely knew was very near. "Hon, I'm still at the shop. I have here *with me* (that meant, "close enough to hear what you say, too, so for heaven's sake don't shriek out 'Oh, no, not *him* . . .'") the new manager of the mill, Harry Morgan."

"Oh, I see." Those three words were an accomplishment for someone who was thinking, "I don't believe it!"

The new manager of the big Weyerhaeuser mill at Snoqualmie Falls—that was the only possible translation. An important person, not only to the 750 families with breadwinners on the mill payroll, but to every businessman in the Valley whether he sold goods or services to the mill directly or to the men whose pay checks came from the mill. The man who had been the manager during our first eight years in Snoqualmie had never stopped in at the newspaper which for forty years had been recording the births, deaths, marriages, social events and club activities of the men who worked at the mill; he had never visited the *Record* before we came, though he'd been the community's very important person for twenty years.

The *new* manager was sitting in Ed's office!

"I'm going to bring him home for dinner," Ed was saying into my disbelieving ear.

I murmured, "That will be fine." Once, several years earlier, I had dared to extend a dinner invitation to the old manager. It was accepted by his wife, and I won a five-dollar bet with a friend. The evening of the party his wife called to say they couldn't come, and I had to give back the five dollars.

"And hon, he'll stay overnight. I told him it was silly to go to a hotel when we've got a guest room." A vivid mental picture of our guest room shot into my mind. In the center of the scene, dripping surrealistically over the edge of the ironing board, yesterday's lamb roast I'd planned to heat up for supper tonight. . . . Softly enough not to be overheard (I hoped) I croaked, "You aren't coming home right away, are you?"

"It will be some time before we get home," Ed replied, inverting my emphasis neatly and raising his voice to a level of abundant good cheer. "And don't worry about dinner. I'll pick up some steaks and two or three nice fresh crab."

"Crab!" I exclaimed in a muted moan. "Not crab . . ." Washington's Dungeness crab is the most delicate seafood imaginable, New England lobster notwithstanding, but it must be cleaned, cracked, painstakingly shelled. Why did Ed always bring crab when he came home late and with company for dinner?

"Harry says he likes crab," Ed replied. The new manager might conceivably be quite a different sort of man from the manager we had known, for he had been "mister" to everyone.

I looked down at my apparel. Blue jeans, sneakers, a plaid shirt. Some hostess gown. And I also knew the answer to another question. I shouldn't have been ruminating at the open refrigerator door, I should have combed my hair. "When *are* you, uh, you two, going to get here?"

"Fine, fine," Ed replied heartily, "but we won't be home for a while. Say, 6:30."

Forty-five minutes . . .

I hung up and ran to the guest room. For all of us, it offered too easy a solution to the problem of what to do with an object which shouldn't be thrown away. "Guest" room! Tailor's shop, playroom, library annex or an outsize locker for sports equipment—it was all of these. I couldn't imagine storing a guest in there along with everything else, even if he were agile enough to make it past the badminton set to the bed.

"Johnny, get the vacuum cleaner," I bawled toward the living room. "Hi, help me put away the movie projector and the croquet set. I'll move the ironing but you get a dust cloth."

"Don't get so shook, Mom," Hi replied calmly. "We'll help."

It was a busy three-quarters of an hour. Though there were two full shelves of clean sheets, the double width linen for the guest-room bed was at the bottom of the last pile I went through. In frantic haste, with both boys repeatedly shouting over the roar of the vacuum cleaner, "Don't get so shook, Mom," we transformed what had looked like a warehouse for St. Vincent de Paul into a reasonably clean guest room. At least it would meet the needs of our overnight guest if he didn't have to hang anything up in the closet or put anything away in a bureau drawer.

I even had time to change into a dress and put on some lipstick, and at 6:30 I was sitting in my yellow chair, breathless, it's true, and not absolutely sure that my slip wouldn't show if I raised my arms, but sitting, nevertheless, with something of the appearance of a hostess waiting for dinner guests.

The new manager was the second in a year. His predecessor, a warm, likable man, had been moved up in the company organization after only a year in our Valley. It was the manager who preceded him who was responsible for my apprehensive feeling about this man Ed had called "Harry."

"I don't want you selling your newspapers in the company store," he had commanded by telephone the year we purchased the *Record*. "I'm running a sawmill up here, not a newsstand."

"The building in which I left the papers," Ed replied, "was a grocery store."

That ended the conversation, and also most of the printing business we had been receiving from the mill.

The new manager Ed had addressed by his first name might be as likable, as smiling, as the interim man who'd been with us for only a year. Or he might be a throwback to the man who had run a sawmill, and nothing but a sawmill. In any case, I was ready for him, and, *mirabile dictu*, on time.

As it happened, way ahead of time. Six forty-five, 7:00, 7:15 . . . At 7:30 Ed walked in alone.

"Gee, I'm sorry, hon, but when I got to the market Ken wanted to talk to me about their ad for next week. Bigger than usual, lots of Easter specials. I was there longer than I realized. Here, though . . ." He handed me a small package. "I brought the hamburger."

"Hamburger? Where's the new manager? Mr. Morgan? Where's the steaks and the crabs?"

"Oh, he had to change his plans," Ed explained, with remarkable objectivity considering the look he was getting from me. "He got a phone call from home, and decided to start down this evening instead of waiting until tomorrow."

A week later, the witching hour for the interesting telephone call was ten minutes of seven.

The previous hour had been frenzied. I was in the shower washing my hair when Hi reminded me that the eighth-grade ballroom dancing class began at the Y at 7:15 and John asked—also shouting through the bathroom door—if I could drive him over to the county pool for the evening swim period. These two recreation centers were approximately five miles apart. The second car was in the garage with a sick battery, so the only automobile was the one Ed was driving.

"Turn on the oven," I shouted back, with shampoo running into my mouth. "Get dressed to go . . ." TV dinners would be quick. I could put my hair up in bobby pins in fifteen minutes, if I hurried. Ed would be home any minute, so there would be a car. . . .

I was rinsing my hair when the telephone rang. Under the noisy stream of water I heard the bell faintly, and then running footsteps to the bathroom door and Johnny's urgent message: "Hey, Mom, it's for you!"

I turned off the water, wrapped myself in a terry cloth robe, and dripping and barefoot, slid across to the telephone.

"Charlotte, this is Ken. At the market."

"Yes, Ken."

"Ed asked me to telephone you. He was just in here to get some meat. He's bringing the new mill manager home to dinner. They'll be there in twenty minutes."

Ken was a good personal friend. Ed and I had had lunch with him a few days earlier and I had described the frantic preparations the boys and I had gone through for a house guest who didn't arrive. The steaks, the crabmeat, and the anticlimactic package of hamburger—Ken knew it all and had agreed, with obvious insincerity, that husbands are clods.

"Oh, sure, Ken," I agreed. "Don't tell me what he bought. It was steaks and fresh crabs."

Ken sounded surprised. "Why yes, that's what it was."

"Nice try, Ken."

"No, really. Ed *is* bringing the new manager home for dinner. He had to pick him up at the mill and he was in a hurry, that's why he asked me to telephone."

"Well, you are a good friend to do it."

"Charlotte!" Ken exclaimed in an anguished tone of voice. "Listen, Charlotte, don't you believe me?"

"Of course I do. I believe that Ed told you to telephone me. I believe he told you to tell me just what you've said. It's just like him, the dog, and you too, Ken Langton."

"Listen! They'll be there in twenty minutes!"

I shook my sopping head. "No, they won't be. I know my husband. He'd put you up to this, but it would never be more than a joke. Well, thanks for calling. You might have fooled me, if it hadn't been for last week. . . ."

I slid two frozen dinners into the oven, and while they heated I put up my hair. Confident that Ed would be home in time to drive the boys to their respective rendezvous, I decided there was no need to dress presentably so I got into a nightgown, a comfortable if somewhat tattered robe, and bedroom slippers. In this ensemble, completed by the numerous rollers, clamps and bobby pins which bobbled metallically on my head, I greeted Ed when he and the new manager walked through the kitchen door.

Some women may think husbands are children, with

just a few simple, predictable emotions any female can foretell. *My* husband looked at me as if I were chic, beautiful and twenty-one, and said proudly, "Harry, this is my wife."

Whether it was a superb example of self-possession, or whether after sixteen years of marriage this startled creature whose wet head sprouted three kinds of aluminum thingamajigs was, to him, a wife to be proud of, it didn't matter. Ed's expression, his proud if improper introduction, restored my confidence. And the new manager, the big man in the community, the mogul of the mill, was just as composed as Ed was. He was young, blond, and reminded me of someone.

"Hon," Ed continued, "this is Harry Morgan."

The new manager stepped forward. Smiling warmly, he said, "I guess you don't remember me. But my sister Dorothy was in Longview High School when you were."

I gave a loose curler one absent-minded flip and then forgot all about curlers, worn old robe, nightgown, and my shiny, scrubbed-looking face. "*That* Morgan family? Why didn't I think of it? Your father was the manager at Longview. . . ."

"Sure. Harry Morgan, Sr."

"And your sister was at R. A. Long, I remember her, and my father knew your father. . . ."

"You lived in the old Tennant house on the lake. . . ."

Ed thrust a large package into my hands. "Here's the steak and the crabs."

"Thanks." Holding the package in both hands, I asked the new manager, "Weren't you in my sister Jacqueline's graduating class?"

"Yes, I was. Where is she now?"

"In San Francisco."

Ed stepped between us. "Why don't you two sit down?"

"Yes, please sit down," I said, dropping the package on the table. "Where's your sister Dorothy?"

"In Yakima. She married an attorney. . . ."

Eventually the publisher of the local newspaper and the manager of the local sawmill drove Hi and John to their classes, while I changed into a skirt and sweater. Then the three of us cracked the crab—Ed, Harry and I.

iii

As a girl of ten or eleven I had often clipped coupons out of magazines, filled them out as the advertisements instructed, and mailed them. The purpose was to obtain free samples, and at one time I owned an unusually fine collection of face creams, breakfast cereals, patent medicines and coffee substitutes, none of which was ever to be opened, of course.

When Johnny spent an entire afternoon clipping coupons, I had assumed his purpose was roughly what my own had been some thirty years earlier. I overestimated the economy of our times (free samples now cost twenty-five cents) and I underestimated my son.

I was working at the *Record's* reception desk one afternoon when a stranger walked in and asked to see Mr. Groshell. He was out of place in Snoqualmie; I couldn't fit him into any category of strangers who want to see the editor. Dark suit, white shirt, highly polished shoes, plain gold cufflinks in spotless French cuffs, a pale gray Homberg—expensive, a bit on the conservative side, and yet there was a little of the Mississippi riverboat cardshark mixed with the banker. His voice was deep, his manner suave.

Should Ed be "in" or "out"? I couldn't decide. "I'll see if he's free. May I tell him your name?"

The man drew a fine lizard-skin wallet from the inside pocket of his suitcoat and presented his business card.

David R. Stilworth. Business Opportunities—and a Portland, Oregon address.

I was still uncertain. "If you are interested in advertising in the *Record,* perhaps our advertising manager could help you, rather than Mr. Groshell?"

He shook his head politely. "No, it has nothing to do with advertising. Mr. Groshell wrote to *us.* I've come up from Portland in order to interview him."

For an instant I stared at him rudely. Business Opportunities. The thought flashed across my mind that this might be connected with the Mr. Harvey in California who had twice inquired about buying the *Record.* Whatever action Ed had taken without my knowledge, it had brought this gentleman two hundred miles for an interview. "I'll tell him," I stammered. "He may be—able to see you by now."

Ed was wrapping packages of printing, a job which often falls to the fellow who owns the place as well as a Master of Arts degree. I held out the card.

"Who is it?" Ed asked. "What's he want?"

"He said *you* wrote to *him.*" I added with a touch of malice, "He is here to interview you."

Ed gave me an odd look and rubbed his hands on his trousers. "How many stripes on his sleeve?" he quipped and headed for the front office. I was right behind him.

"How do, sir . . ." Ed said, extending his hand. "What can I do for you?"

"We got your letter, Mr. Groshell, and I came to talk to you about our enrollment plan."

Ed grinned. "I'm sorry, but enroll where, if you don't mind telling me?"

The richly dressed Mr. Stilworth appeared to be genuinely surprised. "You are Mr. Groshell? Mr. John Groshell?"

I drew in a deep and trembling breath. Coupons. Those fool coupons Johnny had clipped so diligently. Ed didn't know about them.

"Oh, now I understand. You have the wrong Mr. Groshell. John Groshell is my son."

"This is the address he gave. Care of the Falls Printing Company, Snoqualmie. He does work here, doesn't he?"

Ed nodded solemnly. "Oh, yes."

"I gather he isn't here today, however."

"That's right." Ed knew nothing about the coupons, but his instinct was sure. "He went out on a special assignment."

How very true, I thought. John was assigned to second base on the church baseball team.

"In that case, I'll come back tomorrow."

"It might be best to telephone first," I suggested. "He's often out of the shop."

The man nodded. "I will. But I have to return to Portland as soon as possible. Would you give me his home telephone number, please, so that I can call and make an appointment tonight."

He departed, with a last suave smile and dignified inclination of the head.

"What," Ed said quietly, "has John got himself into?"

I told him about John's afternoon of coupon clipping. "I had no idea what he was sending away for."

"Now I understand something else." Ed reached under the counter to a wire basket in which mail and messages for the family were filed during the day. "This."

There were four envelopes addressed to Mr. John Groshell. They were all thick, all from organizations which, like Mr. David Stilworth, offered some sort of business opportunity. John had mail from a school for meat cutters, a distributor of coin-operated vending machines, a hotel chain.

It might be called a youthful prank, I reflected, a typical twelve-year-old game for a rainy Saturday afternoon. But the spread of letters on the counter reminded me strongly of our last serious conversation, when John had begged to know *why* he couldn't work in a grocery store, and *why* couldn't he have a job of his own, as Hi did?

John was too practical a boy to believe that any of these coupons would bring him a real job. The make-believe was admitted when he wrote "Mr." John Groshell and by telling the truth, but only part of the truth, allowed these organizations to conclude he was a grown man working at the Falls Printing Company. But the desire behind the silly coupon clipping, the youthful urge to get out of the nest, to fly—that *was* real, so real that apparently there was some satisfaction to John just in imagining it was possible.

"Silly kid," Ed muttered, "what all did he send for? I wonder."

"It's too bad that man came all the way from Portland," I said, instantly rushing in to conciliate, "but I doubt that Johnny had any idea sending a coupon would bring someone here in person."

Ed shrugged. "I don't care about the man from Portland. If he actually made the trip to see Johnny—and I don't know how true that may be—without doing any checking whatsoever ahead of time, then he's got more to learn than Johnny has."

"Doesn't it strike you that John must want very badly to get some sort of a job?" I hesitated, and added lamely, "I mean, a job independent of—our shop?"

Ed gave me a thoughtful, half-frowning glance and turned toward the backshop. "Don't get tied into knots about John's desire for independence," he said curtly. "He'd like it, of course, as long as it didn't interfere with baseball, basketball, golf, or bowling."

That evening Ed and John sat down at the table for a talk, heart to heart, man to man.

"Dad, it didn't say on the coupons that they would send a man here. It just offered to send information."

"That may be," Ed replied, "but your request led them to believe that you were sincerely interested. *I'm* not going to cover up for you, and neither is Mom. You got into this, you've got to handle it."

"All right, I will," John said, "but what am I supposed to do?"

"When he telephones, *you* talk to him."

The phone bell that night rang for John. He accepted it stoically. From the living room we heard him say, "Yes, sir, I sent for information. No, sir, I'm twelve years old. No, sir, I didn't know you would . . . I'm in the seventh grade. No sir, I'm four feet nine. Well, thank you. Yes, maybe in a few years. Yes, sir . . ."

After the call, Johnny came into the living room. "I guess everything's all right, Dad."

"Next time," Ed said wryly, "watch what you send for."

The incident was closed, he had cleared himself. Johnny's face brightened. "Yeh, I will, Dad."

Casually, Ed asked, "You still have the idea you'd like to work in a grocery store?"

Johnny glanced at me quickly, then down at the floor. "Well, no, not exactly. I mean, sometimes."

"Don't let me stop you."

Johnny's eyes met his father's. "You mean, if I wanted to apply for a job someplace, like a store, you wouldn't be mad?"

It was a sharp thrust, so simple, so boylike, so much more direct than Hi's efforts to bring his father out into the open with a long debate.

Ed shook his head. "No, I wouldn't be mad. I would have talked to Ken about it when I stopped at the market this evening, but I thought you'd prefer to look into it yourself."

"Gee, thanks, Dad . . ." and they shook hands.

In my yellow chair, I bent my head over the newspaper. Present, but not participating. Watching, listening, but only from the outside. When it was time to go to bed, Johnny would come to me to say good night. Ed might ask me how my writing had gone today. But in the moment of understanding I had just witnessed, the moment I'd hoped for, I'd had no part. I kept my eyes on the newspaper, but for a few minutes it was hard to read.

12

THE MANNER in which Ed drove into the yard and parked the car told me that a serious difficulty had arisen that day. The faithful old station wagon knew this driveway as an aging horse knows its own barn, but he steered like a man trying to follow handwritten directions in a neighborhood without street signs. Having parked the car, he sat several seconds behind the wheel, staring absently at the dashboard. To a wife watching her husband through the kitchen window, it was very clear that it had been more than the conventional hard day at the office.

"You look beat," I said as he came through the kitchen door. "What happened today?"

"Nothing much."

"But *something* . . ."

He shook his head wearily. "Let's not bring the office home at night. I'm tired, that's all."

Physical fatigue never made him act tired; discouragement did. "If you'd just tell me . . ."

"It isn't much," he repeated edgily. "The Teletypesetter acted up. I think I've repaired it, but it doesn't matter anyway. I haven't got a Teletypesetter operator."

The Teletypesetter had brought automation to the Falls Printing Company. It consisted of two parts: the first, a machine with a typewriter keyboard where a typist-operator transferred news copy onto rolls of perforated tape; the second, a small accessory to the Linotype which "played" this perforated tape through the big typesetting machine so that it performed like a player piano without a pianist. As weekly editions of the *Record* grew larger, this marvelous electronic gadget became more and more important. Without it, our lone Linotype operator would have to set all news stories by hand, a virtual impossibility unless he worked two shifts a day.

"No Teletypesetter operator?" I asked.

"Her little boy is sick. Measles or chicken pox, I can't remember. Anyway, something good and contagious, so her little girl is bound to catch it just about the time the boy is ready to go back to school."

"Can't we find a substitute?"

He shook his head. "I've tried to locate someone. Looks like I'll have to keep my shop going without automation for a while."

He didn't emphasize it, but the expression "my shop" jarred me so badly that for a moment I couldn't think of anything to say. *I* haven't got a Teletypesetter operator, I'll have to keep *my* shop going. . . . The words discarded the partnership I had been trying so anxiously to preserve, at least in part. Our sons were fighting for their release, and in a sense had won a discharge, but there remained the "we," Ed and I, which I had felt gave meaning to our newspaper, our business, our shop. *My* shop . . . The significant little word rejected my share of the partnership.

"I'll come down in the morning and run the Teletypesetter."

Perhaps Ed had spoken deliberately, perhaps his choice of words was subconscious. In either case, he was shutting me out, and I was frightened.

"No need to."

"But you know there is!"

"You've got your writing to do. I'll get along."

Again the exclusive, lonely, first-person singular. The need to pull us back became urgent. "I don't have to write tomorrow, or for two weeks, as far as that goes," I said doggedly. "It's been some time since I operated the perforator but I'll pick it up quickly."

"It's been three years since you operated it," Ed replied. "No, you stay home. You need your rest, and punching tape all day is not the way to get it."

I hadn't remembered when I last worked at the Teletypesetter, but he did, and that fact stung me. "I would have worked on it if I'd known you wanted me to. But you've never asked me, you haven't mentioned it . . ."

"Look, Mom, that's just what I've been saying. I haven't needed you, and I don't now. Stay home. Write, take a nap, read a book. I'll run my shop."

The words festered throughout a restless night. In the morning I awoke more determined than ever to restore the kind of side-by-side relationship which Ed apparently felt no longer existed. He agreed reluctantly when I insisted at breakfast that I go to the shop with him, and so at eight o'clock I sat down at the perforating machine, as anxious as a freshman trying to please her favorite teacher.

The difficult aspect of operating a Teletypesetter is the necessity of decoding perforated tape. By noon the vertical rows of six little dots, spaced differently for each letter of the alphabet and each mark of punctuation, were beginning to jump around on the tape. By three or four o'clock my head was bursting with the pressure of concentration. But I was making good. The rolls of finished tape, representing box after box of news copy, proved I was really helping.

Several times Ed came into the corner where the machine and I were locked in combat and said, "You better knock it off. Remember, the man who installed it said two hours was enough for a beginner."

"I'm not a beginner," I retorted. "Apparently you've forgotten, but I'm the first operator he trained."

Because the second or "player piano" attachment on the Linotype had been out of repair, there was a backlog of perforated tape which had been punched by the regular operator the day before. Thus it wasn't until five o'clock in the afternoon that the first of the tape on which I'd worked so laboriously was run through the Linotype.

The results were useless. Meaningless words, jumbled sentences, dropped from the machine. Perfect robot that it was, the Linotype relentlessly spewed out just what the little dots I'd punched called for, in stick after stick of crazily scrambled letters.

I was still in my corner, pounding feverishly on the keyboard and feeling cleansed and ennobled by the wonderful effort I had been making. When Ed approached I looked up eagerly, waiting for his praise.

"Have you punched tape all day without checking a roll on the Linotype?"

"It didn't occur to me . . ." I stammered. "I was typing so carefully . . ."

In the grim, tight tones men use when they are determined not to shout, he said, "An operator should run off part of a roll before she starts punching another one. This is particularly important when the machine has just been repaired."

"You mean, all the tape I worked on today is no good?"

"That's just what I mean. Would you get up, please, and let me see what's wrong."

In a few minutes he had found the cause of the trouble and had made the necessary adjustment. "If you'd checked your first tape," he said, "I could have done this at nine o'clock this morning."

"Are you blaming me because something was wrong with the machine? When I was only trying to help?"

"It was a long day's work," he said quietly, "and a hard one. But six rolls of useless tape is no help."

"I'll do it over again tomorrow."

"Don't be silly."

"Someone has to," I retorted. "I will."

"This is not the place to discuss it." He walked away and disappeared into the backshop.

So much for my desire to please, I thought bitterly. So much for recreating "our shop."

When we drove home, we were both angry, frustrated, and tired to the bone.

The day begun so hopefully had turned into a debacle, for which we instinctively blamed each other.

"I *am* coming down in the morning," I said as soon as we were on the road.

"I'd rather you stayed home."

"I am aware of the emergency just as much as you are. It's no time for me to 'stay home,' as you put it. Incidentally, I do *work* when I'm at home."

"Now you sound emotional and there's no need for it."

"I'm emotional because you told me, back at the shop, that I hadn't been any help at all!"

"That's not what I said," he retorted. "I was taking a realistic view of the day's output. There was nothing personal about it."

"Haven't I ever helped at *your* shop?"

"It would have been a help," he said grimly, "if you

had observed one of the most basic rules of the job you were trying to do. Check what you've finished. *Always* check what you've finished."

"I worked hard!"

"Mom, for heaven's sake," he said wearily, "what are you trying to prove to me? In the first place, I didn't want you to come down to the shop. . . ."

"*Your* shop!"

"All right!" he broke out, "all right, *my* shop, if that's the way you want it!"

"No, it isn't. That's why I sat there all day long in that hot, airless little corner, and skipped lunch, and got a headache, because I wanted it to be ours, not yours. For *your* sake, not mine! Prove something? Of course I was. I was trying to show you that I'm with you, I haven't walked out or left or turned my back. And then you tell me I was no help at all. How do you suppose I feel?"

By this time we had reached our driveway. Ed parked the car, turned off the ignition, and turned to face me. "If you feel the way I do," he said in a tight, husky voice, "you've got a rotten headache and you feel slightly sick at your stomach. The boys are at home. I'd like to drop this discussion right now, if you don't mind."

"Gladly. Except for one last point. I am going to come down tomorrow."

"Do as you like," he said as he stepped out of the car.

Angry, miserable, and coldly silent, the two of us went into the house.

In the morning, I sat down at the fiendish machine and began to retype every news story I had copied the day before. As soon as I had finished the first few yards of tape, I took the roll to the backshop to be run off. This time the Linotype produced sensible words and sentences. My work was beyond criticism. Without looking at Ed, I returned to my corner.

We passed each other, we talked when necessary. He no longer wanted me here, I no longer expected praise—but the tape moved along smoothly, and I stayed with it, stubbornly hammering out line after line.

At noon, he approached and said stiffly, "I'll take you out to lunch."

I shook my head. "No, thank you, I'm not hungry."

An hour later he returned. "You're overdoing it," he said gruffly. "Come on, I'll get you a sandwich."

"I don't want anything."

About three o'clock he reappeared. The Teletypesetter perforator is equipped with a small light similar to the bulb which illuminates a Linotype keyboard. Leaning over my shoulder, he turned it off.

I wheeled around, ready to argue, but his gentle, somehow hopeful expression took the fight out of me. "How many times do I have to fire you?" he asked softly.

The machine was a Teletypesetter, not a Linotype, and the month was May, not October, but the symbolic action of turning off the light was a poignant reminder of the afternoon he had "fired" me and then bought me my beloved basset hound, Jo.

"It's only three o'clock. I'll work for a couple of hours more."

"You can't." He took both my hands and pulled me up out of the chair. "We've got to go get a basset hound."

"We've *got* a basset hound!"

"Only one," he said, grinning. "I think it's time Jo got a little sister."

"You can't be serious!"

But he was. In fact, he had already placed a telephone order for a five-months-old female puppy by the name of Lee. With my exclamations of disbelief providing a gasping obbligato for the trip, we drove from the Falls Printing Company in Snoqualmie to the Bassetts' Basset Kennels in Woodinville, where Mrs. Bassett pointed to the yellow daveno in the living room and said, "There she is."

Some basset hounds learn to sit up, others lean heavily on their ability to look sad, but Lee had a special skill—she smiled. With her large bloodshot eyes resting on us lovingly, her fantastic ears tangling with her front paws, she tilted her head to the side and threw us a wide, lopsided smile. Her upper lip wrinkled upward, trembling joyously; her chin bobbed as it shared the upper lip's message of unbounded love and admiration.

"We really ought to think this over," I said stoutly, but five minutes later I was carrying her to the car.

As we left, Mrs. Bassett warned us that the older hound might be jealous of the new arrival. It was important, therefore, to give Jo reassurance. We must not ignore or neglect little sister, but we must pay particular attention to big sister's emotional needs. . . .

The meeting between Jo and Lee was cordial enough, but very brief, since Lee spotted Jo's dish almost immediately. The dish was empty, but Jo was concerned with the principle of the thing. Hair standing up in a spiky ridge along her spine, she beat little sister to the target.

Lee smiled at her nervously, backed away, sighted the hassock which was Jo's private and exclusive couch, and bounded toward it happily, ears flapping. She gauged the height correctly, but not the breadth; though the hassock was three feet in diameter, she plunged right over it, landing with a thudding, slapping sound on the floor at the opposite side.

Solid and dignified as a dowager, Jo strutted to the hassock, lifted herself neatly and sat, right in the middle of it, looking the other way.

Lee's long face quivered self-consciously as smile after smile tried to tell Jo that she'd only been kidding. Jo ignored her. Sighing tremendously, Lee lay out flat on the floor, nose pointed directly at the hassock, and fastened sad red eyes on her queenly big sister.

"Which one of them are we supposed to reassure?" Ed asked dryly. "I think Jo took this round."

As a puppy, Jo had been confined to the kitchen overnight, but once household etiquette had been mastered she was allowed to sleep in the living room. Lee had also been reared as a house dog, for she was an only child (a rare creature, indeed, in a breed which normally produces litters of ten to a dozen pups) and Mrs. Bassett assured us that she hadn't dishonored the living room since she was six weeks old. Ed and I decided, therefore, that we would let both dogs have the run of the house at night. This was important, we felt, to shoring up their sense of security.

The next morning we rose to find a puddle on the dining-room floor.

"Mrs. Bassett was a little overconfident," I said as I rolled up a newspaper and reached for the puppy. "Bad girl," I keened, swatting her hindquarters. "Bad girl." Jo looked on righteously.

The second morning we found that the same offense had been committed. "I'm sure it's only temporary," I insisted as once more I laid on with the newspaper. "After all, she's only five months old, and this is a strange place. She'll become adjusted in a day or two."

Every morning for a week the living-room rug was desecrated and every morning I whaled the puppy and told her she was a bad girl.

At the end of the week, Ed decreed that Lee would have to spend the night in the kitchen. "You know what happens to the children of permissive parents," he explained. "Later they write articles telling everyone that they really wanted to be disciplined."

So Jo retained her freedom, but that evening we shut Lee into the kitchen.

In the morning we learned how devious are the expressions of a basset hound's sibling rivalry. There wasn't a spot in the kitchen, but the living-room rug bore the usual water mark.

"Jo!" I exclaimed indignantly. "Why, you tricky, jealous, mean, naughty, selfish . . ."

With dignity unsurpassed, Jo walked past me to the back door, where she waited, chin up, to be demoted to the backyard.

"Well?" Ed asked. "Where's the rolled-up newspaper? Aren't you going to punish her?"

"Gee whiz," I said in a hollow voice, "I just can't. *You* do it."

"I can't either," said the hard-hearted disciplinarian I married. "How can you spank a dog who stands there looking as if she were going to refuse a blindfold?"

ii

We were still adjusting to life with two basset hounds, which is, in the aggregate, about a hundred pounds of dog, when Ed came home one evening with a baby duck. The explanation, he told me quickly, was a classified ad.

A subscriber by the name of Mrs. George Morton had obtained a clutch of duck eggs, but she had no incubator or broody hen, so she used her husband's electric heating pad for the hatching. Mr. Morton had been so exercised over his wife's misappropriation of his property that he had placed a "want ad" in the *Record*.

I remembered the ad. The gist of it was that the Mortons needed a setting hen if Mr. Morton's neuralgia was to be eased, and Mrs. Morton, claiming that this public notice was very embarrassing to her, had sent word via her husband that sooner or later she was going to get even with the *Record's* editor.

It appeared that time was a great healer. Two or three weeks had passed, and she had not only forgiven Ed but proved it by leaving a baby duck on the doorstep of the *Record* office, a gift for the editor.

"His name is Skeezix," Ed decided. Duck and carton were installed in the corner of the kitchen, and Ed announced huskily that this was the nicest present he'd ever had and no one was to lift a finger against his duck or there would be trouble, and how.

"Are the basset hounds and the duck going to sleep in the kitchen together?"

"The dogs can stay outside," Ed said firmly. "This is May."

I pointed out that in May we often have nice weather, for ducks, so why not put Skeezix outside?

Ed stood firm, at least for two days and nights, and then it was apparent even to a loving owner that the young mallard's early training would have to be continued in the back yard.

"Those blamed hounds might hurt him, though," Ed decided. "I'll buy some lumber and some heavy hardware cloth and build him a pen." Cost of materials was about three dollars. Building time: the free afternoon Ed had promised to take me to the golf course.

After a few days Ed felt the basset hounds had accepted Skeezix, so the duck was released from the high-rent district and allowed to waddle merrily around the backyard, sampling the strawberries. But it was clear—at least to Ed—that he was lonely. "We'll have to get another duck for Skeezix to play with," he decided.

"He's quite happy playing with the strawberries," I said in an unpleasant, wifely way.

Ed's reply was that a duck needs another duck, and so

the next morning, as a surprise, Hi used a dollar of his savings to buy one of the ducklings a North Bend reader had advertised for sale. This young fowl had an athletic build and he was twice as big as Skeezix.

"I think," Hi said as the second duck was liberated, "that a good name for him would be Wheaties."

Skeezix admired Wheaties immediately, but two problems arose. Being so much bigger and stronger, Wheaties almost trampled his pal to death when the cracked corn was served. Secondly, Wheaties wasn't satisfied with our backyard, for through the chicken wire he could see other fields, other yards. He led Skeezix astray, and instead of one lonely duckling, we had no ducks at all.

I thought of the loss in terms of the three-dollar pen, the five dollars worth of scratch feed, and Hi's dollar, but Johnny was concerned on another count. "We've got to get Dad's duck back. Maybe if I buy another duck and put him in our yard, he'll make such a racket he'll call the other ducks back." So Johnny invested a dollar of his savings, purchased Wheaties' brother from the reader in North Bend, and installed him in the duck pen in our back yard.

The newcomer—Johnny named him Frenchy because the black marking on his head looked like a beret—began to bleat immediately. The response was remarkable. Within minutes Skeezix came paddling through the underbrush like an unlimited hydroplane rounding the south turn, and an hour later Wheaties heard the call and was back in camp.

For a time there was peace at the duck ranch, though of course we had to keep buying shelled corn and the water which should have been poured on the rosebushes went over the ducks instead. Skeezix and Wheaties patrolled the area around the duck pen, communicating noisily with Frenchy, and after a few days we decided that the prisoner was now acclimated and could be safely released. We opened the duck pen and Frenchy strode out, giving us a baleful look. Like the Pied Piper of Hamlin he quacked commandingly, turned south by east, and led Wheaties and Skeezix off the premises.

On a warm evening later in the week we were seated in the living room reviewing the case with a houseguest from California, Father Ned O'Neill, when our neighbors telephoned. Neighbors, on our road, are generally separated from each other by five or ten acres of ground as well as patches of alder and evergreen trees; the family nearest to us isn't within shouting distance except on a calm and windless day. Had we lost some ducks? they wanted to know, because three ducks were in their backyard, sitting on the outside of their duck pen, looking in.

"Two big strong white ducks and the third is a kind of sickly looking mallard?"

"That's right," the neighbors agreed. "You better come and get them."

Hi and Johnny were spending the week end with friends, and Father O'Neill was of the opinion that duck-catching is not a one-man job. "You can hold the gunny sack, and I'll chase them towards you," he insisted, so at ten o'clock at night he and Ed set off for the neighbors. I couldn't find a gunny sack so I provided the posse with an old pillowcase.

It was my error to stay home, for, according to the neighbors, it was a spectacular chase. Father O'Neill, a Navy chaplain for many years, stood six feet three inches tall and had muscles to suit. The *Record's* editor was shorter but had traveled with a carnival as the wrestler who takes all comers—the local tough received twenty-five dollars for staying in the ring for ten minutes, fifty dollars for pinning Ed, nothing if Ed pinned him. However, Skeezix and his pals were almost too much for both men.

They raced around and around the neighbors' yard, miraculously avoiding a head-on collision. Duck No. 1 was caught, and after a few more laps, Duck No. 2, and they had just secured No. 3 when the bottom fell out of the pillowcase.

The neighbors contributed a stout gunny sack, and Ed and Father O'Neill took up the chase once more. The ducks were pretty scared by now, and it was totally dark, but after a few more trips around the circuit the two men captured them and brought them home. The ducks didn't appear to be ruffled by the experience, but their pursuers collapsed in easy chairs and called for water.

Soon after, Wheaties and Frenchy were butchered and placed in the freezer so that the boys' memories would be fogged by other interests by the time I served duck for dinner. The cause of it all, little lonely Skeezix, died what might be called a natural death. I found him one morning at the door of my writing house, where, it appeared, he had choked to death on a slug.

iii

A woman's forty-second birthday never receives the publicity which traditionally accompanies her twenty-first, though she may now be twice as wise and twice as understanding, as well as twice as old. My own, on May 22, 1958, was not heralded with garlands of flowers nor with any specific references to the year 1916, but to me it was memorable for two reasons.

The first was a visit to the Tumor Institute, where a new set of x-ray films showed that the treatments seven months earlier had been what the doctor termed "completely successful." That is, the calcium deposit in the hip socket had been dissolved.

"Then why," I asked, "does it still hurt?"

He shrugged. "Because there is still a bursitis."

"What do I do about it?"

"There are shots. Novocaine. Cortisone. As I told you, that's not our business here. You'll have to see an orthopedic man." And he moved toward the door.

Did the man ever smile? Had he ever said something silly or irrelevant, or thrown confetti or worn a paper hat? "Forty-two years ago today," I chirped, "I was born right here in this hospital."

He did stop and turn around. "Is that so?"

"It's quite fitting to be here today, don't you think? The homing instinct."

"When your hip gives you pain, go to bed and put a hotwater bottle on it. . . ." He nodded curtly and disappeared.

After I'd dressed and was leaving the bare white stall for the last time, I tried the nurse. "It's my birthday," I told her. "Funny to spend it here . . ."

She grimaced good-naturedly. "I spent *my* birthday here, but I didn't tell everybody about it."

"I guess this is my last trip to the Institute."

Unexpectedly, she dropped her capable hand on my shoulder and gave me a playful, friendly little push. "Good," she said, "and we don't want to see you again, you hear?"

I was through at the Tumor Institute—that was sufficient reason to remember the day. When I got back to the Valley, I found a second.

"You're not to cook dinner tonight," Ed instructed me. "We're going to go out. I've already phoned the restaurant and asked Cec to save four of the best steaks in the place. Incidentally, I've got a birthday present for you."

We gathered in the living room for the presentation. "Hi, John, keep Mom in her chair until I bring it in from the car. . . ." The boys watched me owlishly, for apparently they knew more than I did, and a few minutes later Ed returned, carrying a large cardboard carton shipped from a taxidermist in Seattle.

"I hope this doesn't give Real George a bad spell," Ed remarked as he opened the carton. "To a slightly un-balanced pussycat this might look like one whale of a father symbol."

The box contained a prime cougar pelt, ninety-two inches long from nose to tail tip. The massive head had been given the "natural" finish; that is, the glaring yellow eyes were glass, but the whiskers, both the soft ones and the quill-like feelers, were the big cat's own and so were the terrible bared teeth. The fur had good color—warm, rusty orange down the back, soft oyster-white under the belly—and had not been "shaved" or dyed.

"It's one of those Jim McFarlane shot last November," Ed explained. "He got three one day, and a fourth the next. They were all in prime condition."

Hi and John cleared the big oak table in the middle of the living room and spread the skin out. Even with four wide leaves extending the table to its greatest length, the cougar's tail hung over the edge.

"Where did he shoot this one?" I asked.

Ed pointed across the meadow to the base of the moun-tain. "Right over there," he said, grinning, "about a mile from our house."

Hi and John presented their gifts—a bottle of cologne and a manicure set—and we were sitting around the table, a relaxed, amiable little family group joking together on Mother's birthday, when Ed glanced at his wrist watch.

"It's later than I realized. Boys, get washed up and put on clean clothes. We'll be leaving in fifteen minutes."

Their facial expressions changed instantly. The easy laughter died and a look of tense watchfulness took its place.

"Where are we going?" Johnny asked uneasily.

"Out for dinner. Steaks. Better get going because I told Cec we'd be there at seven."

They hesitated. They didn't look at each other, or speak, but in that significant pause Ed knew as well as I that for some reason they didn't want to come with us.

"What is it?"

Hi shook his head. "Nothing, Dad. Come on, John, let's get dressed."

"There is something, and I'd like to know what it is."

"No, really, it's nothing," Hi said stubbornly.

"If you were telling the truth, you and John would have raced each other to the bathroom shouting, 'Steaks! Yippee!' Instead of that you stood here and stared at me. You've got something on your mind. All right, what is it? I want to know."

"Can't I keep *anything* to myself?" Hi burst out. "It happens to be private."

"It isn't really private, Hi," Johnny said anxiously. "I mean, we might as well tell Dad."

"Maybe it isn't what you'd call *private*. O.K. Parents are always keeping things to themselves. They always decide what we're supposed to hear about and what we shouldn't know. For gosh sakes, this time I just don't want to talk about something. That's fair, isn't it?"

Ed said stonily, "Go to your room and change your clothes. And when you're ready to go, you better be smiling."

Hi turned and walked stiffly toward his room.

"We didn't know about going out to dinner," Johnny said apologetically. "We knew it was Mom's birthday and all that but we didn't know there were any plans for the evening."

Hi stopped dead and turned around. "John!"

"I'll tell if I want to, Hi." John faced his father. "We were going to go to a skating party. The girl Hi likes . . ."

"John!" Hi shouted from the dining room. "That's my business, not yours."

"Well, I was invited, too!"

Silence. We'd shot off in four different directions, and every route had ended abruptly in a cul-de-sac. My birthday celebration had caused trouble, but it *was* my birthday, Ed *had* planned a celebration. Ed's questions had been inspired by a sincere desire to solve the boys' problem, whatever it was, but he had been pushed to the point of issuing an order. Hi had bogged down in pointless rebellion and Johnny, caught between loyalties, was completely frustrated. We were in four separate little blind alleys and didn't know how to back out of them.

The heavy silence continued until Johnny and Hi had gone into their own rooms at the other end of the house.

Then Ed muttered, "What in the hell did I do this time?"

"Nothing. Except raising your voice, giving a command."

"Do you blame me?"

I sighed. "I don't blame you, no. I think you could have handled it a little differently."

"I didn't know about a skating party. Did you?"

"No, of course not. You know I would have mentioned it if I had."

He struck his left palm with a clenched fist. "They should have told us about their plans. Confound it, they should have told us."

"Or maybe," I said wearily, "you should have told them about *your* plans. In any case, I'd much prefer letting them go to the skating party."

"Oh, absolutely, so would I." He sat down, angrily slapped his knees with his hands. "You'd better let your boys know that they don't have to come with us."

Habit was strong. I had always welcomed any chance to soften the harsh word, to intercede, to interpret; how often had I rushed in saying, "Please, let me handle it," because that was my only hope of keeping peace?

I pulled myself out of the yellow chair, and started toward the boys' room. I would tell Hi to be smiling, when he came out. I would assure Johnny that his father wasn't mad about the skating party. And later, when Ed and I were having dinner and his temper had cooled, I'd get him to see the boys' points of view. . . . Suddenly I thought—No, I won't. I stopped, turned around, and walked back into the living room.

"Ed, I'd rather that you talked to the boys. While you're driving them to their party, I'll change and fix my hair."

"I didn't do too well a few minutes ago, according to you."

"You came close to losing your temper, and you didn't need to."

"All right, that's what I said. You handle the whole thing. You like to."

I sat down in the yellow chair. "No," I said quietly, "I won't. It's my birthday."

He looked at me curiously but didn't reply.

"Furthermore," I continued, more boldly than I felt, "you are taking *me* out to dinner. I am going to be your date. Me, the girl you used to know. Not the mother of your children, not *Mom*. Miss Smoot."

I closed my eyes. When Ed stood up and walked past me, I opened my eyes and moved, as quietly as possible, toward the bedroom, where I took out my prettiest dress, and my best earrings, and my good perfume.

iv

It was impossible to find a Father's Day gift to compare with the present Ed had given to me on my birthday three weeks earlier.

245

"Shirts, ties, shaving stuff and cigarettes," Hi recited unhappily. "What can we get for Dad that we haven't given him for Christmas and his birthday every single year?"

"His editorial this week said the best Father's Day present is a kind word."

"Oh, sure," Johnny said, "and when we ask him what to get for him, he always says he doesn't want anything but good spirit all day long or something like that. Mom, you know if we didn't buy something for him, his feelings would be hurt."

I nodded. "Yes, he'd feel—forgotten. But he doesn't want expensive gifts, I'm sure of that."

Hi said flatly, "He's not consistent."

"Of course not," I snapped. "Nobody is."

Hi said quickly, "All right, Mom. Gee whiz, don't take my head off. I just made an observation."

"You just criticized your father. Now come on, let's get those presents wrapped. . . ."

So, to a man who had received shirts, ties, shaving stuff and cigarettes at Christmas, we presented a shirt, a necktie, a safety razor kit and a carton of cigarettes. Hi and John brought the packages to the kitchen after a leisurely Sunday breakfast; Ed opened them slowly and appeared to be delighted with the contents.

The morning was sunny and warm. We sat at the breakfast table for some time, the back door open, the basset hounds stretched out side by side with their noses pointing toward the fresh June day. Daydreaming, the boys chewed on the last bits of toast and sausage, and Ed and I drank an extra cup of coffee. The gift wrappings were piled around his chair, the tablecloth was littered with toast crumbs and spots of jam, and outside the house, on the wide sill above the sink, Real George stretched and settled down to keep a sleepy eye on us through the window.

"Nice day." Ed yawned.

"It's Father's Day," Johnny said in a bright tone of voice I should have suspected. "What would you like to do, Dad?"

Ed shook his head. "Nothing. Absolutely nothing."

"Well, I mean, it's up to you. You can have your choice."

Ed sat up straight. "Thanks, old man. My choice is just what I said. Nothing."

"Gee, Dad," Hi said, "don't you want to *do* anything?"

Ed was alert now. "Like what?"

"Anything you want, Dad."

He said dryly, "Like, just for instance, the double-header the Rainiers are playing today with Sacramento?"

That was it, of course.

Both boys nodded vigorously, although they were watching their father's face for a storm warning. He shrugged and said cheerfully, "I thought that subject might come up. O.K. That is, if it's all right with your mother."

I was mentally giving myself low marks for understanding my sons. "Certainly, let's go. I'd love to go. I've got to give you credit, Father dear. Even when I knew something was up, I didn't think of the baseball game in Seattle."

"Someday," he said softly, "someday, you'll pay attention when I tell you that I know about boys."

"Whoops!" John skidded away from the table. "You mean, we can go to the game today?"

Ed nodded.

Johnny's boyish impulsiveness was not for Hi, who stood up slowly, squared his shoulders and said, "That's swell, Dad. O.K. if I invite a girl?"

"A girl?" Ed exclaimed, blinking up at his older son.

"If it's O.K.," Johnny put in hurriedly, "I'd like to invite one, too. *That* girl's sister."

Ed threw me a look of simple, unvarnished bafflement. "Girls," he repeated, "on Father's Day."

"Someday," I whispered, "you'll let me tell you something about boys *and* girls."

So the wonderful little family outing, the father-son holiday for four which Ed had approved out of gratitude for a shirt, a tie, some shaving stuff and cigarettes, went off smoothly for the four of *them*—Hi, John, and the two girls. During the thirty-mile drives to and from the ball park, the boys and girls occupied the rear section of the station wagon; they talked incessantly, but not with the couple on the front seat.

At the ticket booth Hi got in line in front of his father. "We're paying our own way."

"Here, I'll take care of it."

Hi ignored the five-dollar bill in his father's outstretched hand, dug into his pocket and pulled out four crumpled singles. "No, Dad, I use my own money for dates."

Entering the ball park, the boys guided the girls to seats several rows below and to the right of ours. "Nobody sits with parents," Hi explained, sotto voce.

We had attended a good many baseball games, for Ed had been a sportswriter at one time and Hi and John had been baseball fans from the first grade on. I was the one who went along, too, the fourth member of a fan club in which one hundred percent attendance was three. When we went to the ball park, Ed always sat between the two boys. They talked baseball, marked scores on their program, shouted at the umpire. Their interest in where I was sitting came alive only when they had to crawl over me on the way to buy some popcorn. Game after game, I clung passively to the outer rim, as functional as a mastoid bone or an appendix. I liked baseball, or I wouldn't have gone at all, but for the company I was in, I didn't like it loudly enough to be noticed.

This Father's Day at the ball park was a new experience. Ed and I sat together. The boys who had so earnestly sought his comments about the game, who had pestered him with questions and begged for stories about baseball, weren't even within shouting distance; there was nothing for it, he had to talk to me.

For the first few innings, he didn't say much. Even one hundred feet away, the boys were closer to him than I was and he kept watching them and reporting exactly what they were doing.

"Hi just went down below. John's staying with the girls. Here comes Hi, he's bringing lemonade. Looks like Hi's girl wants a hot dog. He's going out again. He's looking for a vendor. Ye gods, he isn't even watching the game, and there are three men on base . . ."

It was wonderful how much of the game Ed could see without interrupting his observation of the two couples below. "*Now* it's orange pop. . . . Good night, Hi's buying popcorn, too. . . ." His voice softened. For the first time he turned and really looked at me. "For the girl," he said, smiling. "Not for himself. I think he kept a program but everything else was for the girl."

"She's a very nice girl."

"She's hungry," Ed said, grinning. "He'll be broke by the end of the first game."

"But he's learning something. Children are naturally self-centered. Sometime they've got to start learning to adjust to others. Hi is thinking of what someone *else* wants. Maybe it's because she's a pretty girl, but it is a step in the right direction."

For a moment Ed seemed to forget the ball game, and even the quartet which had absorbed all his attention from the moment we sat down. "Don't worry, hon," he said, covering my hands with his. "I know they're growing up, and I can see what's happened today is part of it. I miss the flattering attention of my sons, I'll admit it. But you don't have to offer me some sort of consolation."

"It isn't much of a Father's Day for you."

He smiled. "It isn't what I expected. But nothing ever is, is it? *Hey look,* a home run!"

From then on, he watched the game, not without talking, however, because he soon found there was a great deal about baseball that had to be explained to me.

13

We hadn't owned the Falls Printing Company very long
before Ed discovered, to his discomfort, that some of his
fellow citizens didn't pay their bills. During our first year
or two in business for ourselves, matching what we received with what we owed was often impossible, and because of our own circumstances Ed assumed all his non-
paying customers were actually good Joes struggling along
as we were. Eventually he began to observe little incon-
sistencies in this picture.

There was many a good Joe on his list of overdue accounts, but there was another type, too; viewed unsenti-
mentally, he was simply a guy who didn't intend to pay
until he had to. He wasn't the poor man; the chronic
deadbeat was more often a man or woman who wouldn't
pay, than one who could not. So we came to realize, like
anyone with a little business of his own, that survival
sometimes depends not only on offering a good product,
or winning the confidence of the community, or even on

being a hard worker or an honest man. The question was, how good was he at collecting bills?

Ed hadn't anticipated this aspect of owning a weekly newspaper and printing plant. He hadn't expected to be a janitor, either, but he met the challenge of broken plumbing without flinching whereas bill collecting was a chore he detested from the beginning, and for several years he wouldn't, nor would he permit an agency to do it for him. Dunning your neighbor in a small town has a personal, embarrassing quality, but Ed's aversion for bill collecting would have been just as strong in a big city. He simply didn't like to ask anyone for money.

Ed was far more inventive at finding excuses for such people not paying, than they were themselves. "His wife has been sick. . . . He'd pay me if he could. . . . He just bought some new equipment, but once he's got it paid off. . . . He's good for it, just give him time. . . ." Some of our hard-headed (and not noticeably poor) business associates gave him advice, and Ed swore he would follow it, but when it got right down to asking for payment he approached the most renowned local deadbeat as if he were a little old lady who was saving up for a new wheelchair.

A series of incidents drove him to his first campaign. A man who had been too strapped to pay his bill for printing delivered two years earlier bought a fine new car. (At that point, our automobile had a mileage reading of 97,000 miles.) He ran his own business on a strict cash-and-carry basis but charged printing and advertising at the Falls Printing Company and had for eighteen months. His spiritual cousin was a merchant who collected six percent interest on all charge accounts not paid in full by the fifteenth of the month, but paid his bill at the *Record* once a year, reluctantly, and without interest. A wealthy woman, widely admired for her efforts in behalf of charity, asked for a discount on five dollars' worth of stationery, and a storekeeper who had boasted repeatedly that he could spot a bad credit risk from across the street, closed up his own shop and took his wife and his cash register to another state, no forwarding address. . . .

Ed was brooding over these inequities when he came home for lunch one day. "This morning," he said, "I compared our bank balance with the amount of money we need to pay this month's bills. We're $1,200 short."

"We could borrow from the bank."

Ed nodded. "That's what I had decided to do, until I went through the ledger and added up fifteen or twenty of the accounts which have been overdue for six months to two years. They came to a lot more than $1,200."

Knowing that the *Record's* publisher could advise his best customer to go fly a kite far more easily than he could collect $3.50 for a subscription, I asked, "Well?"

"Why should I borrow money, at six or seven percent, in order to meet current expenses, when there are twenty people who have actually been borrowing money from me, for months, and in some cases, for years, without paying any interest at all? No, confound it, I am not going to the bank. I'm going out and collect bills."

"You're scaring the daylights out of the parakeet, but I think you're absolutely right. My only observation is this: Can you do it?"

"You don't know what a tiger I can be," he trumpeted, burning the roof of his mouth on the bean soup. "I'm going to go right up to Bud Durish and say, 'Look, you jerk, the printing you ordered last year was for a club and I happen to know the treasurer gave the payment to you. How about it? Do you pay me or do I talk to the other officers?'" He bit savagely into a tuna fish sandwich. "That'll wake him up."

"You'll have to collect several of those old accounts from women."

"Sex," he said uneasily, "has nothing to do with bill

collecting." He swallowed the last of his sandwich and drained his coffee cup.

"But what if they cry?"

His effort to shrug off that possibility was only partially successful. He muttered something like "Who cares?" but his eyes were those of a cornered man.

"Well, they *should* pay, and there's no question about that. Tell me, tiger, when do you start?"

"As soon as I've had lunch."

I waited until he began licking his forefinger so he could pick the bread crumbs off the tablecloth and then I asked, "Isn't it time to start collecting those bills?"

"I said I would!" he replied, half indignant, half injured. "Won't you even let me finish my lunch?"

I glanced at his dishes. "You've already finished."

He looked down at the cup and plate, astonished by their emptiness. "What? Is this all we're having?"

"It's more than you usually eat."

"Well for gosh sakes," he said petulantly, "haven't we got any cookies?"

I found two or three damp, stale remnants at the bottom of the cookie jar, and Ed ate them with the brooding concentration of a two-toed sloth. "It's lunch time now," he explained. "No point trying to make calls, everyone will be out. . . ."

"Lunch time! You've been stalling for so long it's halfway to quitting time!"

"That's what I mean," said my hard-boiled husband. "Not much time to make calls this afternoon, everyone will be heading for home."

Before he actually started out, he said he had a cold coming on and probably ought to take a hot bath and go to bed. He thought it would be a good idea to repair the screen door, right this afternoon, a job he'd neglected for six months without being visibly conscience-stricken. But eventually he got into his jacket, picked up his black list, and cheery as the end man in a Florida chain gang, he left to collect overdue accounts.

That first collection drive did make it possible to pay our own bills and preserved our status quo at the bank, where for a good many years it was always a seller's market as far as the Falls Printing Company was con- cerned. Every year thereafter, not on a particular date but just when the list of accounts long overdue was too long for one page of 8½ x 11 typing paper, Ed flexed his muscles, gritted his teeth and went out to collect.

It never occurred to me to volunteer, nor did Ed ask me to try my hand at a chore so distasteful to him. My effort to take care of the bookkeeping (I lasted for two weeks) had proved to everyone's satisfaction (especially mine) that I just couldn't handle figures. I could make change, if the customer helped me calculate the sales tax, but so falteringly that more involved financial matters, such as bank statements and accounts receivable and bill collecting, were not considered my cup of tea. In eight years I had collected one overdue bill.

My success was scored at the reception desk of the *Record* office. A woman interested in politics had placed advertisements for her favorite candidate, who, unfortu- nately for us, lost the election before we mailed our state- ment. Printing bills for wedding invitations are frequently hard to collect once the great day is past. When his daughter is married and gone, the father of the bride often loses interest in some of the minor details through which the happy alliance was accomplished. Political ad- vertising runs a close second; the politician who is elected feels secure for a certain term and much less concerned than he was earlier about what the local newspaper might say about him, and the defeated candidate, like the father of the bride, has nothing more to lose. The woman who charged fifty dollars' worth of advertising for a man who didn't make it, ignored our statements every month for a year. Then she opened a small shop, needed business cards and statements in a hurry, and expected to charge them, too.

Perhaps it was my position within the fortress of the reception desk which made me so daring, for she was a good deal bigger than I, but I held the package of printing in my arms until she had counted out cash to cover not only the current order but the political advertisements of the year before.

On another occasion—it was a rainy night in June— a small circus came to town for one performance. The main tent was pitifully small, the tent which housed the menagerie and side show was even smaller, but it was a circus, nevertheless, and Hi and John wanted to see it. Ed and I dropped them off and drove to the shop, where we planned to work while the boys were seeing the show.

We'd been at the newspaper office for an hour or so when Ed looked down the street toward the circus and said wistfully, "I have a hunch that's five dollars we can cross off the books."

The five dollars they owed us was insignificant in terms of cash, but significant, it seemed to me, as a symbol of the way I'd let Ed carry too large a share of the burden. "Look," I said impulsively, "I'll go collect for the ad."

Ed smiled weakly. "Do you mean it? I'll give you a one hundred percent commission."

So I set out for the circus grounds, rehearsing all the way the series of simple actions I was about to take. I would find the owner, hand our bill to the owner, insist on cash, take it, thank him, walk away . . .

Rain had changed the meadow where the circus stood to a field of slippery mud. The deepest puddles had been filled with coarse sawdust, but it was already reduced to a sticky rust-colored mush which clung to the shoes and left ugly traces on the wet grass. Rain was pouring through the cracks and holes in the roofs of both sad little tents. In the smaller one, a wet midget elephant stood patiently at her tether, waiting for her part in the performance; her hide had a whitish, scrofulous appearance and her curving backbone stood out sharply, like the exterior plates on a small and sickly dinosaur.

A portable ticket booth had been set up between the two tents, and from the stout, husky-voiced woman seated inside I learned that the owner was in the "big tent" and probably in the middle of his act. Anyone else in charge? She shrugged expressively. There were only four of them in the troupe: the owner, who sold candy and did a clown act; his daughter, who was the acrobat and also rode the elephant; the boy who took tickets and handled the trained dogs, and herself. Was she the owner's wife? Hrrumph, she answered, if I wanted anything I'd have to see *him*.

I continued through the wet, flapping entrance of the main tent, but my desire to collect five dollars from this threadbare little outfit had deserted me. Inside, the spectators huddled together on a set of bleachers which faced three show rings. In the first, a wire cage contained a few terriers, shivering with nervousness or with cold; apparently their act was to come. In the farthest ring, a plump girl of sixteen or seventeen, dressed in a pale green ballet costume, was seated in a swing suspended from the insufficient framework which also supported the tent. The act was in progress in the center ring, where a man in haphazard clown make-up and a seedy dress suit was talking to a pair of boys—my sons, Hi and John.

"Thank *you* for assisting me," he was shouting in a nasal sing-song aimed at the top row of bleacher seats. "Now I'll give each of you a sack. . . ." Hi and John solemnly accepted the large brown paper bags he handed to them.

"And now, both together now, you open up the sacks and whatever's inside, you put it on."

Many spectators had wisely dressed for the weather. Hi and John were wearing yellow Sou'westers and black rubber boots. In such clumsy outfits, they would not find the barker's instructions easy to follow. Hi's sack contained a grass skirt and large, flowered brassière. Johnny was unluckier; one item in his paper bag was a pink bra, the other a woman's girdle.

It was a considerable feat. If the boys struggling with such embarrassing unmentionables in front of a hundred of their grade school pals had been strangers, I would have been a better judge of whether the act was funny. Most of the audience thought it was, and so did the clown-owner, who kept up a high-pitched, mechanical patter throughout the boys' agony.

There was no way to stop the show. An angry mother, charging into the arena to strip the ladies' underwear from her unhappy sons, would be an uproarious addition to the act and an even greater embarrassment to Hi and John than they were already suffering. So I stood at the door, furious but quiet. When the boys had finally wiggled into the garments and, to the hysterical delight of their classmates, wiggled out again, the clown bowed, directed the crowd's attention to the third ring, and hurried toward the wings.

I stepped in front of him. He couldn't have known why this woman with the bill from the local newspaper addressed him in such a cold and venomous tone of voice, but he certainly gave me his attention.

"The show's going on. I've got to bring in the elephant."

"Pay me *now!*"

"Don't know as I've got it here . . ."

"*Now!*"

Deep in the pocket of the old dress coat, he discovered a

nest of bills and change. He was counting the damp and crumpled collection when the last of my anger was swept away by a wave of pity, and I fled.

"Here, here's the dough," he called after me, but I didn't look back.

My defeat was understandable to Ed, but it troubled me because once more I had set out to prove myself and I had failed.

"I shouldn't have let you go over there," he said when I returned, wet and shamefaced. "I couldn't have done it myself."

"That's why I went, and then, as the kids say, I chickened out. I couldn't stay mad."

Ed laughed. "Don't talk to me. I've been preparing myself for another round of collecting, and I've worked up some pretty strong feelings about fifteen or twenty so-called good customers. Don't undermine me."

In the earlier days of a full, family partnership, I had worked at the shop five or six days a week. The unpleasant chore of bill collecting hadn't been a heavy burden in comparison with my own work load. But the picture had changed. Hiring, firing, assignments, editorial policy, mechanical operation—once we had shared these responsibilities, but one by one they had become Ed's, alone. The change was necessary, and desirable; I had been struggling to make it come about, for the sake of the growing, changing boys. But in compensation, I could surely take over this one duty which distressed Ed more than any other.

"Ed, listen. I know I didn't do very well tonight, but collecting from that sad little circus wasn't a fair trial. You've gone through this collection routine for seven years. Number eight is mine. I'll do it."

"Oh, no," Ed replied quickly, "not on your life. You've got enough to do."

"How many accounts did you mention? Fifteen or twenty? It won't take long to call on them."

"It isn't the time as much as the strain. You don't know what a nasty business it is. You haven't been feeling well. You'll make yourself sick."

"Why bring that up again? I was kind of worn out, I guess, but I'm fine now. Even the old aching hip has been pronounced cured by one of the best orthopedic men in Seattle."

"Fatigue is accumulative. You can't be 'cured' in a week or a month. I'll admit I'm a sissy about these bad accounts, but I'm a lot tougher than you are."

"Ha!" I retorted. "Don't you realize that women are far more practical than men? That for plain brass, you can't beat a woman, especially if she's mad? And I am mad, at people who can pay bills, but don't. You've been worrying about this for two months. Why should you have to? Someone ordered something, you delivered it. You shouldn't be placed in the position of begging for payment."

"Yeh, tiger," Ed whistled delightedly.

On Thursday, our bookkeeper made up a list of twenty-five accounts, ranging from debts of $15 to $400, overdue from three months to four years. With that roster in hand, and indignation in my heart, I launched what Hi and John immediately named "Mama's Collection Service."

First I wrote twenty-five personal letters, and seven or eight accounts were paid by return mail. When it was obvious that the remainder were not going to use the self-addressed stamped envelope I'd sent with my letter, I began making personal calls.

Cases of flagrant neglect were not difficult to approach. The deliberate debt-dodger; the blow-hard, who paid for the other fellow's lunch only when the restaurant was crowded; the woman of means, who bought all her clothes in Seattle but at the print shop in Snoqualmie asked for the wholesale price—with these my indignation held up throughout the interview, and waving an old unpaid balance offered a delightful release from tension. But most of the calls disturbed me so deeply that I realized that I *was* making myself sick, just as Ed had predicted.

After a week I was down to the hard core of old accounts. Instinctively I had left the worst to the last, and so progressed from the embarrassing to the distasteful to the downright nasty.

"I thought you wrote books," one woman commented when I called on her husband. "You certainly have lowered yourself when you go out dunning people for money."

"If your husband had lowered himself to the point of paying his bill," I replied, "I could be a lady, just like you."

"I don't care for your sarcasm."

"I'm sorry." My head ached and a large, uncomfortable lump was forming in my throat. "That wasn't meant to be sarcasm. You see, I don't really like to do this. But if I'm willing to spend the money my husband collects by 'dunning people,' as you call it, don't you think I should be willing to dun people, too?"

At that point her husband interrupted the debate by handing me a check. I thanked him quickly and left. I wanted very much to go home, which was as near as I could come to hiding from everyone, but there were seven more calls to make before Mama's Collection Service could conscientiously be retired.

"'When duty calls, or danger, be never wanting there . . .'" I recited unhappily. Spurred by this puritanical slogan, I set out to make one more call.

The storekeeper was in his sixties, a wiry, quickwitted bachelor who, according to local lore, hadn't taken a wife because he couldn't get one at a discount. His store was his

life. In thirty-five years he had built up a hard shell, layer
by layer like an oyster, of credit and clearance sales and
profits gross and net. He was no misanthrope. In the store
he was a spirited conversationalist, especially with female
customers, and occasionally he attended a public fete
such as the annual Fireman's Ball or the American Legion's
Fourth of July dance where there was a good supply of
partners whose tickets had already been purchased.

When I entered the store, he was occupied with two
customers. The situation was the kind that makes bill collecting in a small town such a difficult exercise of tact.
The women were cousins, the storekeeper was related to
the husband of one of them, and all four of us belonged to
the same club, ate in the same restaurants, played at the
same golf course. The women smiled and waved. The
storekeeper, probably remembering that the last time we
had talked I complimented him for being one of the few
men who really know how to waltz, called out, "I'll be
right there. . . ." Sweet harmony, except for one dis-
cordant note; I was there to ask him for money.

"Don't hurry, I'll wait . . ." I said uncertainly and retired
to a distant corner of the store.

He had been in business for a long time. When the
women finally made their purchases and left, he walked
toward me slowly, with a wise smile which seemed to
turn the corners of his mouth down rather than up, and
a shrewd gleam in his eyes. Undoubtedly he had already
guessed my mission. A woman who waits in one spot for
fifteen minutes, when the counters all around are covered
with articles women like to touch, lift, turn around, and
put down again. A woman who waits apologetically, with
a window envelope in her hand . . .

"Well," he clucked, "so you finally got to me."

"Yes. That is, what do you mean?"

One shoulder jerked upward in a nervous shrug. "You've made two, three calls up the street. I heard about it."

I was tired of this hateful campaign. My head was throbbing. "I'm glad you know why I'm here," I retorted snappishly. "Your check would be very much appreciated . . ." and I held out the telltale window envelope.

He accepted it, opened it deliberately, and studied the typewritten statement. "Series of ads, two columns wide, two inches deep." Looking up at me, he added, "Kind of small stuff, ads that size."

"Yes, they were. You told us you didn't need anything bigger."

"Hah! Why didn't you argue me into it?"

"You seemed to know what you wanted."

He smiled, and the nervous right shoulder jumped with amusement. "Newspaper advertising is *your* business. You should have kept after me."

I retorted angrily, "All right, what kind of an ad for this week? The double truck, or do you want to take one page and think small?"

He chuckled. "That's more like it. You been standing here looking hangdog. It's no way to be when you're trying to collect bills." He turned toward the back of the store, saying over his shoulder, "Come on, I'll pay up."

His office was a cluttered, windowless room from which he could watch the entrance to the store. I stood in the doorway, while he sat down at an old rolltop oak desk and with maddeningly slow, deliberate movements uncovered his checkbook, opened it, and wrote a check.

I was beginning to feel ill. My pulse was fast, my face felt flushed, and there was a heavy, throbbing sensation in my neck and shoulders.

"Young lady," he said, "let me tell you a few things. In the first place, stop worrying. Some people are always going to act like they're doing you a favor when they take an ad in your paper. Forget it. No one advertises because he likes the editor, no one's going to stop advertising if he doesn't. Your newspaper can do something for every businessman in town—*that's* what you're selling. In my case, you didn't sell it hard enough, and that was *your* mistake.

"Second place, you shouldn't have let this bill of mine run for so long. The man who owes you money doesn't like you. After a while, he quits doing business with you. You make him pay up regularly, you keep him as a customer.

"And one more thing. About collecting bills. You came in the store when I had two customers. Real politely, you went over in the corner and waited."

I interrupted his lecture. "I didn't want to embarrass you."

He shook his head. "That's just it. Don't be so goldarned nice. You had the perfect setup for shaking me down and you didn't use it. Next time you go out to collect a bill, wait until the deadbeat you're after is all tied up with a good customer, and *then* go after him, loud and plain." He broke off. "Say, are you feeling all right?"

"Not really," I said weakly. "I think I'd better go home."

"Want me to phone your husband?"

"No, no . . ."

"Here, don't forget the check . . ."

I didn't go back for it. The check, the full-page advertisement I was to "keep after him" about—I ran from them both, and down the block to the vacant lot where I had parked my car. Leaning back against the seat, I closed my eyes.

I wasn't going to be sick, after all. My pulse slowed, the uncomfortable flush subsided. I was all right, except for my headache and a childish desire to cry. "Not right here," I told myself, "not in front of everyone . . ."

I drove home slowly. There were too many of these bad moments. The sensible action to take would be to consult our doctor. I would call this afternoon. . . . I parked the car, let myself into the empty house, and in complete control of myself walked resolutely to the telephone and dialed the doctor's number.

At the sound of the nurse's voice, I began to cry.

"Who is this?" she asked. "Who is calling?"

I pressed my hand over the mouthpiece and sobbed helplessly.

"Are you there? Who is it, please?"

But I couldn't stop. Clutching the receiver, I dropped into the chair, leaned against the telephone stand, and cried. "Please say something . . . If you'll just tell me who you are, what's wrong . . ." the nurse begged. Shivering, I replaced the receiver.

ii

The lawn needed mowing. It was a job generally assigned to Hi and John, but I, with my eyelids swollen from pointless weeping, looked out through the window and decided it could not wait, I had to do it, right now.

Like a nervous animal, I paced the cage of our front yard, pushing the roaring power mower in front of me. The job was half done when the mower broke down.

I'm no better at mechanics than I am at bookkeeping. Years before I had decided to surprise my husband by installing a new plate in the electric range, which I did successfully, with the aid of only one tool, a silver knife from my dinner service. When he came home, Ed was impressed with my feat but puzzled, too. "How did you manage to pull out that pigtail when you disconnected the stove?" he asked. "It sticks. Last time I tried I had to fight it."

The surprise, it seemed, was on me. "Pigtail?" I asked. "What's that?"

"Never mind. Just tell me this—was the burner you were working on turned off?"

"I don't know, I didn't notice . . ."

"Two hundred twenty volts," Ed gasped, his face fading to a strange gray-green, and after that it was understood that when something broke down, I had a choice between calling the repairman or waiting for Ed to come home.

Today, however, I was driven by a compulsive desire to finish the job I'd begun. I ran into the kitchen and found the instruction manual. I had always claimed that anyone who can read, can cook, and it's true, if you get hold of Fannie Farmer rather than Marcel Proust. That anyone can repair a gadget who can read the instruction manual which came with it is not such a reliable precept. Manufacturers don't want to tell you too much about the thing they make, for you might find out you can make one, too. In the case of our power mower, the manual described exactly what to do when the machine was working perfectly and didn't admit, even for a second, that it might ever break down.

For two frustrating hours I labored with the ailing lawnmower. It started several times, ran for a few feet, and stopped again. The more obvious it became that I should give up, the more doggedly I kept working. Finally, when I admitted to myself that the machine would have to go to the repair shop, I didn't try to push it to the car. Trembling with helpless rage, I picked it up and carried it, and I was standing beside the car with the seventy-pound mower in my hands when Ed turned into the driveway.

He stopped the car and leaped out, exclaiming, "For heaven's sakes, what are you doing? Put that down!"

"It won't work. I tried to fix it but I couldn't. I'm going to take it back to the dealer."

He frowned. "Why were you mowing the lawn? The boys can do that."

"I *like* to mow the lawn."

"That's ridiculous." In a husband, worry is often accompanied by impatience, and Ed sounded more angry than concerned. "It isn't good for your hip."

"That's not true! I *told* you the doctor said I could exercise as much as I wished."

"All right, play golf, or take a walk. But you don't have to mow the lawn. The boys do little enough around here —that much you can leave to them."

Through such a trivial side issue as the mowing of a lawn we had plunged into the biggest question of all— our individual relationships to our children and their responsibilities to us. It had become dangerous ground, strewn with memories of unhappy scenes. But I was too exhausted, too ill, to be cautious. "Hi and John do whatever I ask them to do," I retorted. "They are very helpful."

"You don't ask them to do enough."

"How can you say that?" I cried, fighting back blindly. "You don't know how I handle them when you're not here."

"I would be very much surprised, and more pleased than I can say, if I discovered that you ever disciplined them, or made any demands on them whatsoever."

"Discipline! I do, but not when you're around."

He said quietly, "Because you think you have to protect them."

"Yes!" I said defiantly.

"From me."

"That's it, exactly!"

His face hardened. "Did you ever realize that protecting them might be bad for them?"

"That's not true!"

"Has it ever occurred to you that some of the sermons you've given me might also apply to yourself?"

"I've never given you a sermon," I replied shakily.

"You can call it whatever you like. But in a dozen different ways you've told me the boys have reached an age when they wish to be independent of us. You've criticized me—yes, you have, repeatedly—for my foolish notion that they have some responsibility to the business we own. They are growing up, you keep reminding me, and it's always with the implication that growing up means growing away—from *me*. But not from you."

"What's this got to do with a lawnmower! I just want to put it in the car and take it to town."

"I don't want to argue, either," he said bitterly. "I just want to come home, and have a hot meal, and take a bath. I don't want to fight about anything, or settle anything. It was a mean day at the shop." He turned away and began to walk toward the house. "It was the kind of a day when a little help would have been appreciated."

"You mean, from me? You don't think I've been helping?"

He shook his head. "I don't know what to think, Mommy. I just said, I could have used a little extra help today. But I didn't get it."

"Collecting bills isn't helping?" I cried after him. "Calling on people, buttonholing people, asking for money. . . ."

He stopped, turned around slowly, and walked back to me. "I didn't want you to collect bills. I tried to talk you out of it. But you were determined that you would. It was like that miserable day with the Teletypesetter, when you seemed to be trying to prove something to me and there was nothing to prove."

"Maybe there *is* something to prove."

"Forgive me," he said huskily, "if I don't understand. Maybe there's more to this than I know. I'll admit it, I'm baffled. You just aren't yourself any more."

"Myself?" I cried out. "What is myself, that's what I can't figure out. I'm the mother of two boys. I thought I'd been doing a good job at that, but you say I'm bad for them. I'm your wife. I worry about you, I love you, but half the time I guess wrong about what will make you happy. Myself? There's no such thing, for a woman. I can help Hi and John be themselves. If I'm clever enough and lucky enough, I can do the same for you. But I'm like a mirror, and right at the moment not a very good one, because I'm tired and I'm acting silly and in about two seconds you're going to say I'm too emotional and you'll be right. *You* tell me what 'myself' should be. Am I good old Mom, is that all, or am I Charlotte, or maybe, sometime, Mrs. Smoke?"

"You're talking foolishness. In fact you've made several statements which aren't true. I know you feel rotten today. . . ."

"I do, yes, I do. But you just said a few things that hurt, and then you reminded me that you meant every word of it. I mean what I'm saying, too."

"I shouldn't have let you go out on that damned collection business. I know what it's like."

"That's only part of it . . ."

"And I think you've been working too hard at your writing."

"You said I wasn't 'myself.' When I'm writing, I am. That's the only part of my life in which I am purely, completely, myself. *Me.*"

"Will you listen to me for a second?" he said gently.

"Yes."

"Let's just tackle one point, and it's important. The way you feel. You haven't been feeling right for a long time, have you?"

"No . . ."

"I think you ought to see the doctor."

"I tried to call," I stammered. "But I couldn't."

It was a senseless statement, but apparently the way I was acting spoke for itself. Ed opened the door of the car. "Get in."

"I don't want to go now! With my face all red from crying . . . In these old clothes . . ."

"The doctor won't care. Please get in."

"But the boys will be home soon! I've got to start supper!"

Ed thundered. "They can get it for themselves! They did when they were nine and ten years old. They could now, if you'd let them!" He shook his head. "I'm sorry." For a moment he hesitated, and then he said gently, "Mrs. Smoky, will you please get into the car?"

In silence, we drove to the doctor's office.

iii

The diagnosis could be summed up in one word: Exhaustion. "Every morning you make out a list of eight or nine jobs you want to finish that day, and every night you check the list and find you've managed to do only five or six of them. You're frustrated, dissatisfied with yourself, so the next day you push yourself a little harder. When you do accomplish every goal you've set for yourself, when you do finish all nine jobs, you immediately add a few extras to the list. You've lived that way for years, and you can't get away with it indefinitely. You're just worn out."

He could prescribe some pills, but the "cure," he emphasized, depended on my learning to live at a slower pace.

"How long?" I asked immediately.

He smiled. "I suppose you've forgotten that that was your first question when you consulted me about your hip:

'How long?' You want to sail into it, fight it out, get it over with. You can't, this time."

"I will *not* go to bed with a hot-water bottle!"

He said ruefully, "Then you won't. But it would be good for you, once in a while."

Learn to relax, take a nap in the afternoon, cut down . . . The prescription for acute frustration was frustrating in itself. "Pace myself," I repeated when Ed and I were discussing the doctor's diagnosis that evening. "That's the vaguest, the most unsatisfactory advice . . ."

Ed said abruptly. "I'd like to ask you something, and I want a completely honest answer."

"Of course."

"There has been a great deal of nervous strain connected with owning a business. Even if we cut down on the number of hours you spend at the shop, this strain won't be eliminated entirely, even without the cursed bill collecting. I've been very proud of this business we own together. But if it's hard on you, if it's responsible for your present state of exhaustion, then I'm going to get in touch with that Mr. Frank Harvey and ask him to make an offer."

"No, that would be wrong."

"To sell the newspaper?"

"To sell it because I'm not feeling well."

"As far as I'm concerned, that's reason enough."

I shook my head. This was a moment of utmost significance, not only for the two of us, but for the absent junior partners, Hi and John. Yet I was feeling drowsy. "I'm not seriously ill. In fact, I'm not sick at all, just tired. Working at the newspaper isn't the cause of it, any more than two or three other things, taken singly."

"I've never answered that fellow Harvey's last letter. His son has probably bought another plant by now. But I can write and find out."

"Not because of me. Only because of you, if *you* want to." This was an important discussion, but I was falling asleep.

"If you sell, you mustn't do it for the wrong reason . . ." My eyes closed, and I didn't try to open them. "What do you suppose was in that pill . . ." I murmured.

"Listen, the shop isn't the reason I'm exhausted. You aren't, the kids aren't. I'm beginning to realize that the one who's been pushing me too hard is the one I was talking about this afternoon . . . Me," I said, as sleep closed in, "me. Myself. You know, that admirable person, the one who gets so much done . . ."

iv

A few days later we went to a county fair in a neighboring town, not to entertain Hi and John because they had left for summer camp, but to prove to each other that we were really learning to relax.

Mama's Collection Service had been suspended, with seven accounts still to be tracked down. I had notified a magazine editor that the article I was writing would arrive a week late. Several appointments which belonged in the duty-or-danger category were postponed and Ed, in order to take me to the fair, crossed off just as many items on his personal list for the day.

It was a hot day, but with a pleasant breeze sifting between the big sheds and tents on the fairgrounds. We strolled from the Holsteins to the Guernseys, from the embroidery to the pie contest, and finally bought two bottles of pop which tasted vaguely like face powder and sat down with them on a bench in the shade.

"If I hadn't fallen asleep in the chair," I began, "I would have said more last night about selling, or not selling, the shop."

"I meant what I said," Ed told me. "If the newspaper is too much of a drain on you, I'll get rid of it."

"No, it isn't. I think I got that much out, even half asleep. The point I didn't get to is this! *You* are running the Falls Printing Company. It's yours, the strain is on *you*. If you write to Mr. Harvey—or to any other prospective buyer, as far as that goes—it must be because you don't want to continue, and not because of me, or Hi, or John."

"Then you've given up our original idea of developing a business the boys would eventually take over."

I took a deep breath, made a quick decision, and said what I'd been too "tactful" or "worried" or peace-loving to say all year. "That *wasn't* our original idea. When we went into business for ourselves, Hi was five years old and Johnny was four. They didn't ask to leave Illinois. They knew nothing about the Snoqualmie Valley or weekly newspapers or print shops. We didn't consult them before we bought the *Record,* or ask them if they would want to take it over in fifteen or twenty years. We left a big city and a big corporation payroll because *we* wanted to.

"And then somewhere along the line we began to say —We're developing this business for our kids. On the one hand we said that they were not obliged to take over the *Record,* and on the other we said we'd never sell the *Record* because we were keeping it for them."

Ed sighed. "Johnny would make a terrific salesman. Hi's feeling for machinery would be a big help in running the backshop."

"How much of a salesman was Johnny at the age of four? What did Hi know about machinery when he was five? But those were their ages when we got our original idea—the idea of working for ourselves rather than for someone else, and to live where we wanted to live, not where we were sent. This is really the heart of what I started to say last night. There is only one good reason for keeping the newspaper, and that's the reason you bought it in the first place, ten years ago. Leave the kids out of it. Leave my aching hip or my cumulative fatigue out of it. The business is *yours*. What do *you* want to do with it?"

Ed grinned. "I'm going to write to Mr. Frank Harvey in California."

"And offer to sell?"

"No. First I'll apologize for ignoring his letters. Then I'll suggest that he let his son find his own newspaper, and I might add that he should concentrate on his orange groves just as I intend to concentrate on the Falls Printing Company."

"Well," I breathed, "that will be quite a letter."

Ed stretched one arm along the back of the bench and let his hand rest lightly on my shoulder. "I, too, had something more to say when you fell asleep last night. About the doctor's statement that you must learn to take things easy. You don't like the idea, I know. I got the same advice when my heart acted up, remember? And I resented it, just as you do."

He pressed my shoulder affectionately. "You loved and admired your grandfather in Boston. Have you forgotten the way he chopped wood?"

I smiled. "No. . . ."

My grandfather, having been a doctor, respected the body's need for physical exercise. Every afternoon he chopped wood. As he grew older, he couldn't accomplish as much. When he was in his eighties, he counted the strokes of his ax, allowing himself a certain number before he stopped and rested for a certain number of minutes. In his nineties, he was able to take very few strokes at a time, and the rest period had to be lengthened gradually. Eventually, he raised the ax for one stroke only, and then

274

rested, and then raised it, slowly, once again, but until he was too feeble to walk outside he never stopped chopping wood. . . .

"Remember him," Ed said gently. "He never quit. But he did pace himself, so that he could keep going for a long, long time."

We talked for some time, wandering sleepily from subject to subject. The warmth of the summer day, the dusty sweet smell of the clover hay in the nearby dairy shed, the slow procession of other couples past our bench, the distant laughter of children in the kiddie park at the other end of the grounds—these simple, pleasant sights and sounds healed the sores of recent arguments. We were two of hundreds at the fair that afternoon; physically we were surrounded by other human beings who bumped into us, drowned out our voices, or pushed ahead of us in a line. But we were held together by an invisible, and for a couple married for sixteen years, oddly innocent awareness of each other. Slowly, taking courage from this feeling, we began to refer openly to various incidents involving Hi or John. With a shock of fear at how far apart we had grown on the subject of our own children, I realized this was the first time in a year we had been able to talk about the boys with no tension between us.

"I'll take you out to dinner," Ed offered. "With the boys at camp, there aren't any baby robins waiting in the nest with their mouths open."

"Let's go home," I suggested sleepily, "and look at the mountain, and have dinner in the living room, just the two of us."

v

We had finished dinner and were watching the shadows deepen on the mountain when a winged creature swifter and smaller than a swallow shot past the window and disappeared under the overhanging eaves.

"That was a bat," I remarked.

"You sound mighty casual."

"Why not? He's on the outside."

Warm summer nights make Snoqualmie Valley bats energetic and hungry. We had often seen them darting back and forth in their nocturnal chase after insects and found it an interesting sight. Not until a dinner party several years earlier had we learned how different from the cool, scientific point of view is your feeling when the bat gets on *your* side of the windowpane.

At this particular party, everyone had grandchildren except the host and hostess. The women were stout, the men were portly, and the atmosphere was rather formal, as if all present were wearing corsets which had shrunk in the wash. I was wondering what important element this party lacked. I didn't know it, but all it needed was a bat.

A gentleman who had said little more than "Hrmph . . ." or "Good Lord, he's a Democrat?" all evening sprang out of an easy chair and yelped, "Look out, there's a bat!"

Even before the rest of us saw the creature, that announcement had an astonishing effect on my dinner party. I hadn't been able to dislodge the women from their side of the living room, where they were discussing their grandchildren, or to budge the men from the far end of the room, where they were deciding what was wrong with the governor. But the word "Bat!" jarred everyone loose and they were mixing energetically in no time.

One woman climbed on a chair, a second kept leaping from the front of her husband to the back of her husband, depending on the angle of the bat's flight. A third woman of stately posture and dignified speech made it to the broom closet in the kitchen in four bounds and bounded back, swinging the homely weapon over her head like a helicopter blade. "Hit him, hit him!" she sang, with the marvelous diaphragmatic support of a female lead in a Wagnerian opera.

I can't remember a great deal more about that evening, except that from there on it was a highly successful party, everyone chatting and joking with the subtle intimacy of persons who have camped together in a wilderness area.

In the excitement of the chase, all our guests had galloped in and out of every room in the house, not without a few collisions, since some were trying to catch the bat and others were trying to get away from it. At last we cornered the animal in the bathroom—two of us—the portliest, most dignified of the gentlemen, and I. He slammed the door behind us. "There!" he shouted, and together we vaulted into the bathtub. While his gentle, bosomy wife on the other side of the door exhorted us to get him, get him, get him, the gentleman and I flailed at the bat with damp washcloths.

"Remember that dinner party?" Ed mused, as the bat made another pass by the front window.

"I was just thinking of it. But tonight the doors are closed, and there are screens on all the windows. We'll have no more bat incidents in this house."

I had just uttered this complacent remark when a bat came down the chimney. He didn't try to avoid us, he flew right at us, like a Kamikaze with his sites on a battleship.

"*Bat!*" I shrieked, and dived under the dining-room table.

"He won't hit you," Ed promised from the other room. Intellectually, I believed him. Emotionally, I couldn't, so I remained in knee-chest position with my head under my arms.

"That's a ridiculous posture," I heard my husband say, "and you're still offering a good target."

I peeked, and found he was right, for the bat had altered his course and was swooping down under the table. Ed was under attack, too, but he rushed to my side. There was a lot of running and thudding and heavy breathing and then I peeked out from under the table and saw that help was on its way.

There was my husband, barefoot and in undershorts, the boys' red baseball caps on his head (both of them, the visor of one pointing ahead, the visor of the other pointing backward, giving the effect of a crimson Sherlock Holmes hat). And he was armed, with a tennis racket. "Don't worry, Mommy," he shouted as he swatted wildly at the bat, "I'll take care of everything."

From room to room the pursued and the pursuer ran, Ed assuring me, even when he seemed to be more chased than chasing, "Don't worry, Mommy, just leave this to me."

"Nice back hand," I commented as he raced by, heading south.

"Oh, dry up," he gasped as he passed on the northbound run.

I was just about to say that he shouldn't borrow his sons' things without their permission when I heard his shout of triumph. "There! I cornered him. He's locked up in Hi's bedroom. You can come out now, dear." We collapsed on the sofa. "I'll get him out of Hi's room in the morning," Ed vowed. "He'll be hanging upside down, sound asleep."

"It's probably just as well that the boys are away at camp. They'd want to keep him as a pet."

"Before that crazy animal came down the chimney, I was thinking about the boys," Ed mused. "About how to reawaken their interest in the newspaper. I've been wrong to confine them to the same old jobs they've been doing for years. When they get back from camp, our ad salesman will be on vacation, and I'll have to cover the advertising beat. I'm going to take Hi and John with me. Maybe not at the same time, but by turn."

I felt myself tense. I wanted to protest—Ed, darling, can't you see that won't work? It's *your* job, *your* newspaper. You said it yourself, remember it, act on it. . . .

Ed was chuckling. "Mrs. Smoky," he said as he put his arm around me, "you sure did look cute down there, under the dining-room table."

The momentary tension dissolved. Not one word against his ad beat idea, I promised myself as I put my head on his shoulder and closed my eyes. Not one single word to spoil this day. "Smoky, you were heroic," I whispered, and turned to be kissed.

14

FOLLOWING OUT his idea to give the boys a new interest in the paper, Ed planned to take them along when he called on our advertisers. Hi was to accompany his father on Thursday, and Johnny would go on Friday. But Tuesday afternoon, when everyone in the shop was working at top speed in the usual prepublication rush, a woman telephoned, asking specifically for me.

"This is Mrs. Groshell," I said absently, writing a headline at the top of a news story.

A pleasant voice replied, "This is Mrs. Bigler at the North Bend Clinic. We're about to perform surgery on your son but wanted to secure your permission."

"My son?" I squeaked, dropping the pencil. "*Which* son?"

"I don't know. The one who was in the river."

Johnny had gone swimming in the Middle Fork of the Snoqualmie. Hi and his good friend Paul had talked about spearfishing in the South Fork. . . . "What kind of surgery?"

"To remove a barb from his thigh."

"That's Hi," I breathed. "Yes, of course, by all means go ahead. I'll be right over."

An injury to any of us frightened and infuriated Ed simultaneously. If the explosion were to be held to a minimum, I'd have to treat this accident casually. I walked across the backshop without hurrying, and told Ed about the call in such an offhand manner that he asked, "How come Hi went to the clinic? Sounds like something we could have taken care of at home."

"I'm going to edit a few pages of copy," I said, "and write a couple of stories. Then I'll run over and see what's going on."

"I've got this press run. Phone me from home in about an hour. . . ."

At the clinic a nurse led me into a room where Hi lay on a table covered with a blanket. "They already did it," he greeted me, grinning sheepishly. "Eight stitches."

"What happened?"

A man in a garage near Paul's had made several three-pronged weapons with heavy wooden handles thicker and longer than broomsticks. They were meant for hunting bullfrogs, but Hi and Paul had decided they would be good for spearing suckers in the deep pools of the South Fork.

Ah, I thought. That explains Hi's request this morning for an advance of four dollars against his September allowance. . . .

So in swim trunks, tennis shoes and underwater goggles, the two boys waded into the river. Hi couldn't wear his glasses. Through wet goggles he squinted near-sightedly at the riverbed but he couldn't see anything clearly. The swift water of the South Fork caught him off balance and he fell on his own spear.

"*Paul!*" he shouted. "Paul, help me!"

The other boy splashed downriver to the riffle where

Hi had tripped and fallen. His first thought was to pull out the spear. Fortunately, Hi knew better. The prongs were barbed, like fishhooks. One of them was imbedded in his thigh to its full length of three inches. Any effort to jerk it free would be unbearably painful and would also rip the flesh cruelly. But Hi couldn't wade to shore, or even move, because he was attached, by means of the barb, to a long, heavy spear handle.

"I'm going to carry you out of the river," Paul said. "You hold the handle of the spear."

At that point Paul got help from a man named Verne Roberts. Verne had been born in North Bend some sixty years earlier. He'd been a logger and a prospector. He'd been a boxer—"Canvas Inspector Roberts, they called me."

Paul stayed with Hi, and helped him hold the parasitic spear handle at an angle which caused the least pain. Verne ran for help, and as a town crier he was loud, fast, and level-headed. In minutes he had dispatched three volunteer firemen to the South Fork, and picked up a bolt cutter at the nearest service station. A fourth man ran to the clinic while Verne followed the firemen to the river.

"Just one snip with that bolt cutter," Hi told me, "and I was loose. About that time the doctor came. He helped me get into his car and drove me to the clinic, and I guess that's when someone called you."

The surgeon came into the room, and with him the doctor who had driven Hi to the clinic. Hi would have to be hospitalized, they explained, probably for three or four days. The depth of the wound made this precaution advisable; there was serious danger of infection.

"I'll take him up to the hospital," the doctor volunteered. In the hall, beyond Hi's hearing, he added, "He's quite a boy. Hasn't shed a tear."

I telephoned Ed from home, as he had asked me to do. The reassuring quality of my report was destroyed by the word "hospital."

"I'm coming right home," Ed said grimly. "I want to hear the whole thing."

I was glad that Johnny had stayed at a friend's house for supper. Once he had asked me, "Why does Dad get so mad?" and now, as then, my only reply would have to be, "Some people do, when they are really frightened." Ed stormed against Hi's crazy spear-fishing expedition, against my letting him try such a fool thing in a shallow river, against teen-agers and spearmakers and mothers and their sons.

I interrupted only once. "Visiting hours at the hospital are from 7:00 to 8:30," I said. "It's quarter to 7:00. Do you want a quick snack before we leave?"

He said angrily, "I'm not going to the hospital."

"Not going!"

"No. If I see Hi tonight, I'll tell him what I think of his stupid, irresponsible behavior. Later, I would be sorry. So I'm staying home."

"He'll wonder . . ."

"If he does," Ed retorted furiously, "you can tell him what I just told you."

I faced a familiar dilemma. If I stayed with my husband, who had worked hard since six o'clock in the morning, I would miss visiting hours. But I sensed that going to the hospital alone would be to challenge the fairness of Ed's decision to stay home. . . . I hesitated, and then suddenly I thought—Why do I consider it a question of "loyalty" to one or the other? Of disagreement, yes. I wanted to visit Hi, Ed did not. Denying myself some part of being Hi's mother was not going to make me a better wife for Ed.

"I'm leaving now," I said. "If he asks, I'll give him your message."

He did ask. When I sat down beside his bed in the corner of the long men's ward, his first question was, "What did Dad say?"

I reported faithfully.

Hi's reaction astonished me. "Sounds like Dad," he said affectionately. "He's right. It was a stupid thing to do. I didn't figure on the rocks being so slippery."

"Dad didn't want to come to the hospital just to bawl you out."

Hi nodded. "Sure. Say, Mom, did you know my doctor writes science fiction in his spare time?"

I left the hospital a half-hour before the close of visiting hours. I'd kept my integrity as a mother, but as a wife I was beginning to feel conscience-stricken about my tired and supperless husband. As I turned off the main highway onto the county road which leads to our house, I saw Ed's car approaching from the other direction. He didn't appear to see me as we passed each other, and perhaps he didn't, because he was obviously in a hurry. In my rearview mirror I watched him make a quick stop, a curt signal, and then, as fast as town ordinance allowed, he turned onto the highway and drove toward the hospital. I doubted very much that he was on his way to give anyone a bawling out.

ii

A week later the boys took turns as their father's apprentice advertising salesmen. Hi joined Ed on his round of calls Thursday, and Johnny on Friday.

I didn't anticipate trouble the day Johnny went along, because he was a compliant, sweet-tempered boy with a knack for avoiding friction. A day's association with Hi might end less peacefully.

To my immense relief, Ed's program for reawakening the boys' interest in our newspaper was carried through without hostilities. Both Thursday and Friday Ed came home with the appearance of a man who has enjoyed a pleasant day, and neither boy looked as if he had tried to "settle" anything.

"Now I'm glad you took the boys on the ad beat," I admitted that Friday evening after Hi and John had gone to bed. "Frankly, I was worried when you first suggested it. But there were no arguments, eh? No scoldings necessary?"

Ed shook his head. "No, none at all."

"Then it *was* a good idea. That is, to get them more interested in the operation of our business."

He sighed. "I could believe that, if I tried. I mean, they were both attentive. They were coöperative. They asked questions about advertising and listened politely to the answers. Yes, if I really wanted to, I could imagine that we were all safely back in the old pattern. The family business, *our* family business, the four of us."

There was a puzzling quality to this answer. "But you don't really believe we are, is that what you mean? Did they seem to feel it was—well, a kind of I-want-to-be-a-pal-to-you approach? Were they resentful?"

"Oh, no, not at all." He looked down at his hands, flexing the fingers a few times as he studied the callouses and paper cuts and small burns collected in the service of the "Valley Blab." "John was a good scout, because he always is. But his interest was pretty forced, except in the stop we made at the sporting goods shop. Hi probably had to try harder than John, but he was polite, too. No, that's not fair to him. He was aggressively interested. He asked questions, and they were good ones. He talked to the various businessmen, and handled himself well. But there were two places where I detected genuine enthusiasm. One was the auto dealer's where two new models were on the floor, and the other was the drug store where cameras were on display. Hi likes cars and cameras. Not newspapers, at least not ours."

"I'm sorry that you're disappointed."

Ed made a wry face. "I'm not, really. They both made an effort. That's more than Hi would have done six months ago. . . ."

I saw a significant change in Ed, too. Six months earlier, he would have been angry because his sons' interest was obviously forced. Now he was accepting, with a touch of gratitude, their not too skillful efforts to play along. The rebellious boy, the demanding father, had met each other half way.

They had done it alone, without Mom, the great conciliator, on hand to keep peace. It struck me that I might also have some growing up to do. The sooner I stopped conciliating, the sooner the young and the old bucks would work things out between them. Maybe it was I, not Ed, who had been clinging to the old family pattern, by believing that a clever wife and a good mother could somehow keep it from breaking up. But it was broken, as an eggshell is broken when the chicken hatches, to allow for growth. The sooner we abandoned the useless pieces, the sooner a new pattern, a new life, would emerge.

"Hands off," I resolved that evening. Let them lock horns, if they have to. A few nights later, shortly before the fall term began at school, my resolution was tested.

The crises in our family always seem to be reached when I am standing at the kitchen sink. This one caught me peeling potatoes.

"Dad, I'd like to get something straight with you," Hi began. "About my column in the *Record*."

My paring knife bit deeply into the potato. This issue had been quieted for a long time by the narcotic of my tactful handling. I guessed what Hi would say next, but it was bound to come as a shock to Ed.

"What about it?" Ed asked.

"I'm starting high school. I'd like to stop writing The Hi-Corner."

A set of well-trained nerves jumped to attention, instructing me to intercede quickly. I pressed my lips together, dropped the potato into a pan of water and picked up another one.

"There's no reason why a high school freshman shouldn't write The Hi-Corner."

"Yes there is, Dad. I'm going to be one of the low men on the totem pole. The older kids would resent it if I tried to make my column express a high school point of view, and now that I'm fourteen I sure don't want to keep on being that *little boy who writes for the paper every week.*"

His emphasis parodied the compliment so many kindly subscribers had given him. It would surely irritate his father.

And it did. As I pared away vigorously on the second potato, Ed said curtly, "Don't look down on anyone, Hi."

"Well gosh, Dad, I mean, I'm *not* a little boy any more. Do I have to keep writing like one?"

"No. You could be our high school reporter. Or if you really believe the older students would resent that—incidentally, I don't, not at all—then you could write straight news."

"When?" Hi exclaimed. "You want me to get good grades, don't you? With homework and everything, when am I supposed to find time to write for the *Record*?"

"Is your job for a Seattle paper a better way to spend extra time than writing for the *Valley Record*?"

This question harked back to such an early stage in the struggle that I automatically began to turn around and join in. I caught myself just as Hi replied, "I've already given up my paper route."

There was a pause, and then Ed asked, "Well, John, you've been his substitute. I suppose you're going to take it over?"

John's voice was shaded with embarrassment. "No, Dad, I didn't figure on it."

"Football practice, eh?" Ed commented dryly. "Basketball, bowling, a few little things like that?"

"That's all right, isn't it?" Johnny burst out rebelliously, sounding remarkably like his older brother. "I like sports. Someday I might even make sports my career!"

I dropped the potato with a liquid plunk and shakily reached for another.

"Fine," Ed said, "fine."

"And another thing, Dad," Johnny continued stoutly. "I suppose I might as well mention it now, while you're talking about Hi's column. Next September, when I go to high school, I figure I'll stop writing mine, too."

"John's Sports Shorts?" Ed asked. "You just got through telling me sports are more important to you than anything else."

"I like *doing* sports, Dad. I never really liked writing about them quite as much as I thought I would."

"In other words," Ed stated flatly, "neither of you boys has any interest in writing for the *Snoqualmie Valley Record*."

Hi answered. "We just have a lot of other things we'd rather do."

"You realize this eliminates you two as partners in this paper?"

"Dad," John said matter-of-factly, "it's really *yours,* anyway."

There was a long, heavy silence, the severest test possible for my resolve to keep still. I could imagine Ed's

angry frown, or was it a look of defeat? Hi was undoubtedly poised on the edge of a new effort to settle
everything, Johnny's face was probably wearing an unhappy, worried expression. . . . Who would speak first, who
would spark the bigger, more destructive explosion?

Ed's calm voice broke the silence. "Well, Hi, so you've
given up your paper route, and you won't be writing a
column. What high school activities do you plan to take
part in?"

"Math Club, I think, and Electronics Club, if they have
it this year," Hi answered. "But most important, I'm going
to turn out for freshman football."

"Football!" Ed exclaimed. "You can't wear your glasses
playing football."

"I'm not going to."

Hi's voice told me he was digging in for a fight. These
potatoes, these stupid, necessary, helpful potatoes. I
jabbed at the next one, grazing my thumb with the paring
knife. Thumb in my mouth, back still turned to the menfolk, I listened for audible signs of a gathering storm.

"You'll be at a serious disadvantage without your
glasses," Ed protested. "Don't take my word for it. Take
the word of an All-American tackle. You remember what
your Grandfather Paul told you the last time he was out
here? Football is a rough sport. It calls for every physical
faculty you've got. A fellow with impaired vision has no
business in the game."

"Paul's going to turn out, too, and he won't wear his
hearing aid."

"You won't be able to see," Ed snorted, "and Paul won't
be able to hear. Why, for crying out loud, do you two get
into these things . . .?"

"I know about my eyesight, Dad," Hi replied. "I'll probably be the worst player on the third string. But I'm going
to turn out."

Another suspension of sound, another void, filled for me by the somnambulistic motions of potato paring. But I still hadn't interfered. All at once it was over.

"It's your decision, Hi," Ed said in a perfectly natural tone of voice. "You're the one who will have to take the lumps. O.K., fellows, how about a game of catch before dinner?"

With unsteady hands, but with a pleasant sense of triumph over self, I rinsed off the potatoes, filled the pan with fresh water, and reached for the salt.

iii

At breakfast Hi said, "I'll make a deal with you, Mom. Since I quit my paper route, I've put on a few pounds. If you help me lose weight so I'll be in trim when high school opens, I'll guarantee that I'll get on the honor roll for at least one term this year."

"Should you lose weight if you're going to turn out for football?"

"Sure. It won't help to be flabby around the middle."

For the next ten days Hi followed a Spartan diet, while Ed and I avoided the bathroom scale and justified our nutritional need for butter, hot rolls and French fried clams. The first day of school Hi weighed himself officially. "O.K., Mom, we did it," he beamed, thumping his flat midriff. "The honor roll, for at least one term."

Ed asked, "Are you still determined to turn out for frosh football?"

"Yes, Dad."

"You're not doing it because you think I want you to, are you? You mentioned another boy whose father was quite a star, and the boy feels he has to play football, but he doesn't really want to. I was *never* a football star, Hi. At your age I weighed seventy-five pounds in my hob-nailed boots."

Hi said, matter-of-factly, "I guess I'm going to be a lot taller than you are, Dad."

"I hope so," Ed said, "but it will be some time before you can take me."

"We'll see about that." Grinning, Hi loped out of the house and down the drive toward the school bus.

When freshman football practice began, Hi had no transportation home because the school busses left at the close of the last class period. This is an insoluble problem in a consolidated school system in which students come from such distances that one of the fleet of a dozen busses covers a daily route of 125 miles. Our home was about four miles from the high school. It was agreed that Ed would pick Hi up on his way home from the shop. When he couldn't, Hi would have to beg a ride or walk.

Fortunately, Ed was able to drive Hi home after the first afternoon practice, for I doubt that the boy could have hiked four miles.

Hi's face was white with exhaustion. "I think I'll lie down before supper," he mumbled and disappeared in his room.

"Why are you so late?" I asked Ed. "The last class is dismissed at 3:30. Did football practice last for three hours?"

Ed shook his head. "Not quite. But the freshmen were still on the field when I got there at six o'clock. They ran for the showers about quarter after six."

"*Ran.* If the rest of them were as tired as Hi, I bet they crawled."

"No, they ran, all of them. Coach's orders. We might as well go ahead and eat dinner. I doubt that Hi will want any even if he does wake up." Before we went to bed that night, Ed undressed Hi and rolled him under the blankets.

The next evening Hi was less tired, but he ate very little.

"You're not trying to stick with that diet, are you, Hi?" I asked anxiously.

"No, Mom, I'm just not very hungry."

"Your lunch period is early, isn't it? Before noon? You ought to have a bearish appetite by now."

"Don't worry, Mom," Hi said. "Just don't worry. I'm all right."

And Ed's quick glance said—Leave him alone.

The same performance was repeated the next night— Hi exhausted but grimly silent, and Ed acting as if there was nothing at all unusual about a fourteen-year-old boy who was too tired to eat and who went to bed before his favorite television show.

In the grocery the next day I met the mothers of two of Hi's classmates, both of whom were far more interested in their conversation than they were in the canned fruit department in which they were standing. "What do *you* think about it?" one of them asked as I parked my basket beside a pyramid of crushed pineapple. "Hi is turning out for football, too, isn't he?"

"Yes, he is."

"Well, hasn't he told you about the way they have to practice?"

I had to admit my total ignorance, and they explained. The freshmen had been getting workouts so strenuous that even the older boys on the varsity squad were shocked and disgusted. The first afternoon, two boys vomited during practice and one of the biggest boys admitted he had a hard time to keep from crying. In the first tackle drill a boy said, "Ouch." Practice was halted while the coach demanded, "Who said 'Ouch'?" and waited until the guilty freshman stepped forward and confessed, "I did." That boy's punishment was two laps around the athletic field, and thereafter two laps was the penalty for making any sound. Boys who were too tired to finish a set of exercises were ordered to start the same exercise from the beginning. . . . "It's no wonder half the boys dropped out the second day," one mother remarked. "It's not right, with thirteen- and fourteen-year-old boys. And why do they have to practice so long? The varsity teams are made up of older, stronger boys who have played football before, but their practice is a half-hour shorter than frosh practice. . . ."

My impulse was to drive to the shop and tell Ed what I'd heard. Instinctive caution kept me from following it. The mother who forbids her son to play football earns the boy's resentment and her husband's displeasure, and often makes herself a little ridiculous, besides. I remembered clearly the woman who considered football "too rough a game" for her boy, but happily agreed to his playing soccer and water polo, because the only physical injury she could visualize was getting one's face messed up during scrimmage. It was not my function to tell Hi he must drop out of freshman football, but I sincerely hoped Ed would do it for me.

That evening Ed listened to my detailed recitation of the complaints I'd heard from the mothers in the grocery store. I hadn't finished before the thought struck me that he knew everything, and more, than I was telling him.

"You know all this, don't you?" I concluded, feeling a tremor of resentment at the all-male pact of silence which apparently existed between Ed and Hi.

"Yes. Not from Hi. Two or three parents have called on me at the office, hoping I would bring some pressure to bear in an effort to stop such tough practice sessions."

"What have you done?"

Ed frowned thoughtfully. "Nothing. And after giving the whole issue a lot of serious thought, I've decided I won't. I don't agree with the coach's methods. I don't think they're wise, or even necessary, with high school freshmen. To me, the emphasis is all wrong. But the coach has a certain goal, and his own way of working toward it. Maybe he's right. Maybe the kids are too soft, and need this kind of treatment to be toughened up. If he's wrong, it isn't my business to correct him. He was hired by the school board. The high school principal is his boss and *he's* the one who will take action, if action should be taken."

"You sound very broad-minded," I replied, "very objective. But I don't like the idea of our son, near-sighted as he is, going through practice sessions that make other kids vomit or faint or leave the field crying."

Ed shrugged. "Mommy, darling, I didn't want the boy to turn out for football in the first place."

"Have you talked to him about this?"

"Yes. I said pretty much what I just said to you—don't stick with it because you think I want you to. I told him he could drop out any time, as far as I'm concerned."

"Apparently he won't."

Ed smiled. "I doubt it. He told me he and his friend Gary have a pact. The first one who quits is a lily liver and the other gets to call him that for the rest of their lives." Ed looked at me knowingly. "If you're thinking that *you* might tell Hi to drop out, forget it."

"I won't," I replied stiffly, "but I'd like to. To be perfectly honest, I feel like issuing an order."

Ed shook his head slowly. "Aren't you the one who pointed out that the boys should be independent? That making their own decisions, launching their own projects, entirely separate from those we do together, is an important and natural part of growing up? All right. Hi made an independent decision. As I told him, he's got to take the lumps."

"He may be injured."

"I know that," Ed replied. "I pointed that out to him.

He says he's in better shape every day, less likely to be hurt. In fact, *he* says the coach is O.K."

Apparently Ed and Hi had talked together a good deal. A wave of loneliness swept over me. "Independence" meant separation. Ed had felt it, and fought it, and translated his sense of loss into the simplest, most direct terms: The boys were no longer interested in the family business.

But mine was a double loss. Their growing up not only deprived me of the close relationship I'd had with them when they were little boys, but every time I had aided them in their adolescent struggle for independence I had helped create a new relationship in which I was gradually being supplanted by their father. I wondered if Ed could guess how with every goal achieved, I had, in one sense, been defeated? The thought came out, though I hadn't really meant to say it aloud. "They're growing up. I want them to grow up. But sometimes I feel terribly lonely."

Very gently he touched my hand. "How do you suppose *I* feel?"

"Not *lonely*. Hi talked to you about football, didn't he? Johnny announced to you, not to me, that he intended to make sports his career. When Hi had to borrow to pay the *Times*, when he was in the hospital . . . I don't know, there is a special understanding . . . Really, you have no reason to feel separated, as I do. Sometimes the three of you pamper me, sometimes you bully me, but I'm always on the outside. *You're* closer to the boys than you've ever been."

"In some ways, in new ways," he said, "but Mrs. Smoke, don't think I can't see how much of it is because of you."

"I feel so—unnecessary!"

"Better take a pill," Ed said affectionately. "And I could use one, too. How do you suppose I feel when Hi points out that he's as tall as I am and he's only fourteen?"

"And I feel old."

"Compared to the old man," Ed said wearily, "you're just a kid."

"And useless! Do you know what Hi said when he was in the hospital and I took him a copy of my new book? He said, 'Gee, Mom, it's got a nice cover, but I'm reading a science fiction book my doctor wrote. I'll read your book later sometime, after I get home.' I haven't even asked Johnny to read my book. I'm sure it would make him dizzy."

Ed grinned. "Hi won't watch the fights with me because he isn't interested in boxing but at the same time he's talking about signing up for the high school smoker. I'll make a deal with you, my dear young wife. You watch TV with me and I'll read your books."

I extended my hand. "All right," I said shakily, "I think we better stick together."

"Yes," he agreed quietly, "I think we better had."

iv

Hi's appraisal of his own value to the freshman football squad proved to be accurate. As a lineman who couldn't distinguish one player from another at a distance of twenty feet, he had some value, for he would plunge, blindly, into his opposite and keep charging those he presumed to be the opponents until the whistle blew. He was on the second team, he explained, only because they hadn't organized a third team, but he did get into a few games and in one of them shortly before the end of the season he was injured.

"Nothing broken," the doctor concluded, "and no irreparable damage, fortunately. Probably be pretty painful for a while but he'll be all right in a week or two."

"How about next year?" Ed asked Hi when we returned

from the doctor's office. "You going to turn out for the varsity?"

Hi grinned. "Listen, Dad, I never did say football was my game."

Thus the football issue was closed, but another came up immediately.

Washington's state legislature convenes every other year for sixty days. The next session was to open in January, about midway in Hi's freshman year, and he announced that he would like to apply for a job as page.

We pointed out that he would have to live alone, in a hotel or boarding house. That he would have to live on his salary. That he'd have to keep up his school work, probably by attending high school in the state capital of Olympia. He'd have to eat out, do his own laundry, get himself up in the morning. . . . Our every question was one of Hi's chief reasons for wanting to attend the session. He would be self-supporting, live alone, and carry full responsibility for school and his job. That was exactly why he wanted to go to Olympia.

"It will be wonderful experience," I said.

"Sure it will. I hope he receives an appointment." Ed smiled at me. "As a matter of fact, I wrote a letter today to the state senator of our district."

"One bird out of the nest," I mused. "But we still have Johnny."

"My dear girl, weren't you listening when we talked all this over at the dinner table? Johnny is living for the day Hi is settled in Olympia because then Hi will invite him down for week ends and Johnny can suit up as an honorary page."

"But it will be two years before Johnny can work at Olympia, too. I mean, this year he won't actually leave home, as Hi is doing."

Ed shook his head. "No, it's gradual. I guess that's

good, for all of us. The kids adjust gradually to independence, and the old folks gradually adjust to losing them."

The day before Christmas a telephone call from the secretary of the state senate informed us that Hi had been hired. He was to report at eight o'clock the morning of January 15 for instructions and his uniform.

The capital city of Olympia is about eighty miles from the Snoqualmie Valley. Hi planned to take the bus, deposit his luggage at the Olympia depot while he hunted for a room, and then (if we insisted) telephone in the evening to give us his address. But we had good friends in Olympia, and welcomed this chance to visit them. On those terms Hi agreed to enter the strange city with an escort of parents.

He sought my advice on one score only. "How do you wash a drip-dry shirt?" I explained, and so, with our blessings, and a pint of liquid detergent, our fourteen-year-old boy left home for the first time.

Ed and I were aware of problems Hi, in his youthfulness, could not anticipate, but we were genuinely enthusiastic about the venture and as Hi's departure drew near, we were both caught up by his excitement. So a new crisis, different from any we'd weathered before, caught me by surprise.

It was the Saturday night before we drove Hi to Olympia, and I was at the sink, as usual. Not potatoes this time. Broccoli.

I heard Hi challenge his father. "O.K., Pops, you weigh more than I do, but I can still take you."

"Is that so?" Ed retorted. "Like to try?"

They began to wrestle. It was in fun, with a good deal of joking and shadowboxing and exaggerated, laughing challenges thrown from one to the other. Johnny watched, admiringly, I thought, with his hands stuffed in his pockets and a wistful expression in his eyes. Pushing, hauling, laughing, Hi and Ed moved from the kitchen into the dining room.

"Hey, the kid's tough," Ed joked. His wind was short, though, and he still hadn't put Hi down.

"I told you," Hi gasped, "I told you I was strong enough to take you."

One of them tripped, or one lost balance—it happened too quickly for me to see. There was the thudding impact of their bodies as they hit the floor and when I turned my head, they were struggling on the dining-room carpet. They were both out of breath but they were laughing.

I returned to the broccoli.

They often wrestled, though it was against house rules. Hi with Johnny, or Ed with Hi, or sometimes all three of them in a kind of three-cornered strong-arm match. Good, healthy, boyish spirits, if a little hard on the furniture. All at once, though I was still occupied at the sink, I knew that the playful tussle had become serious. Talking had ceased. They weren't joking or laughing. It was in earnest now. Not a verbal battle, a "let's-settle-it" argument. This was the real effort to settle something in a physical, animal struggle, the old buck and the young one in a real locking of horns.

For five terrible minutes I leaned against the sink, holding a broccoli stem in one hand and a paring knife in the other. I was afraid to turn around and watch. Not watching, but listening, to the heavy breathing, the scraping and tearing and thudding as they rolled over or slammed against the table leg, and struggled for a fresh hold or a new position—this was almost unbearable.

Of course I wanted to rush in and pull them apart. But the last time they had clashed in an argument I had stuck with my resolve to let them settle it, and they had, not amicably perhaps, but at least on terms acceptable to themselves. It was just as important to stay out of it now.

I couldn't think why I was standing at the sink. The broccoli in my hand meant nothing to me. But I held the position, paralyzed by my wise resolve, and scared. Not of what might happen to Hi. He was sinewy, young; a small defeat at the hands of his father would be erased by the marvelous restorative of youthful egotism. It was my husband for whom I feared, for Ed, who was not growing taller or getting stronger; for whom each contest was a last chance, not a first; who, once defeated, even in so small a way, had nothing more to prove.

The kicking and thumping stopped. Slowly I turned around. Hi was flat on his back. Ed was astraddle the boy, pinning him to the floor with one hand.

The old buck could still win, and to prove it, Ed used his free hand to reach into his pocket, pull out a package of cigarettes, and flip one into his mouth. Still pinning Hi to the floor, he stretched until he reached the edge of the table where a package of matches lay next to an ash tray. With each step of the lighting process, his gestures became more exaggerated. The elaborate study of the match cover, the sweeping movement as he scraped the match head, the little finger delicately poised as he placed the cigarette between his lips . . . He was clowning.

Hi glared up at him, trying to ignore the comedy, and then suddenly he burst out laughing. "Gee whiz, Dad, light the darn thing and get off my stomach!"

"You give?"

"I give."

They stood up, still laughing.

"O.K., Pops," Hi said, "you took me this time. But when I get back from Olympia, I'll be able to take you."

Ed grinned, "Don't wait too long."

Johnny stepped forward. "How about me, Dad? There's still me."

Ed looked down at the younger boy and nodded. "I know that, Johnny. And I'm glad."

Johnny straightened up in a comical imitation of a weightlifter expanding his chest. "I mean, sometime I'll be able to take you."

"Well, you better hurry up," Ed said, "or I might be too old to let you try."

At that point I left the sink. "You just take it easy, both of you," I said, waving a stalk of dripping broccoli. "Keep your hands off your father." And I put my arm around him.

Hi looked at me incredulously. "You got it wrong, Mom. He *won.* You ought to be worried about how I feel."

"Hi," Ed said, as he pulled me closer, "your mother is a girl."

15

Hi BROUGHT a great deal home from the state capital: Passbooks from two Olympia savings banks. Considerable insight into state politics. Important bits of domestic information such as how to hang wet laundry in a tiny room in the Y.M.C.A. and what canned foods can be eaten cold without getting a stomach ache. New understanding of the use of time (he attended high school as well as working full shift at the senate, but made the honor roll). A new sense of responsibility; since he was paid for seven days a week, he worked seven days. And as concrete evidence that he had succeeded when he was on his own and self-supporting, a scroll signed by Washington's Secretary of State, bestowing on Hi the honor of the title "Page Emeritus."

Besides books of senate rules, pamphlets of house and senate bills, rosters, notes, autographs and pictures, he also brought home a camera, and through this unexpected channel, both Hi and John voluntarily rejoined the family business.

During the legislative session, a professional photographer had selected Hi as the model for a rotogravure feature about senate pages. While she was working on the assignment Hi had an opportunity to study the techniques of photo journalism and to explore a well-equipped, professional darkroom. Recognizing his genuine interest, the photographer gave him a camera.

Back home, Hi's conversation was made up of two parts state politics to one part photography, but there was little he could do about the first interest, at least for the time being, except to remember it, while the second could be worked on here and now. We began to hear less about caucuses, senate bills, floor leaders and parliamentary procedure, more about emulsion speeds and focal plane shutters and fixes.

Johnny had received a camera as a Christmas gift the year before, but after writing a thank you note (because he was truly thankful for the gift, and besides there was to be no more bowling until he'd written it) he had stored the puzzling gadget in a protected corner of his bookcase, behind a row of baseball annuals and the cash register bank he had learned to open with a table knife. Inspired by his older brother, Johnny dusted off his photographic equipment and soon Hi was passing along the instruction he had received in Olympia.

The boys had shot a dozen rolls of film when Hi decided they must have a darkroom. "It takes too long to set things up in our bathroom and my bedroom," he said, "and it isn't satisfactory anyway, because I can't really black out my room, even with blankets and dark curtains, and the bathroom is so small Johnny and I can't work in there together."

"What do you have in mind," Ed asked, "other than building a wing onto the house?"

"I thought I'd fix up your workshop."

"My workshop!"

"Dad, you don't use it."

Ed's workshop, even more than the guest room, had become a repository for every unclassified object in the house; it was a kind of terminus, the very last depot before we called the Salvation Army or St. Vincent de Paul, in fact the place where we "put things" when we cleaned out the guest room. Canned goods, camping equipment, suitcases, odd pieces of lumber, and all the various cages, for guinea pigs, hamsters, parakeets, bats and canaries, in limbo, as it were, between the demise of the last occupants and the acquisition of new ones.

A serviceable workbench with plenty of counter space and many good, strong drawers of different sizes stood along one wall, but Ed had used it a dozen times in seven years. A chest of drawers containing his handkerchiefs, T-shirts and socks had been moved into the workshop in order to create more space in the adjoining bedroom; it was right at the door and thus, generally speaking, was the one item the room contained which one could get to without crawling over, or moving, something heavy.

Ed shrugged. "It's true. At this point my workshop is the place where I used to have plenty of socks in the top bureau drawer."

"Cheer up," I said. "Very soon Hi's feet will be bigger than yours."

"If we can turn it into a darkroom," Hi put in eagerly, "I'll clean everything up."

"What about the drawers of type and the old proof press you and John insisted I bring home? That's what's using up most of the space in there. What's to become of the North Bend Printers, Ink, you two were so proud of?"

Hi grinned self-consciously. "I'll help you take it back to the shop. That was kind of—kind of kiddish, Dad, don't you think?"

"Kiddish?" Ed exclaimed. "Less than two years ago you and John insisted on setting up a North Bend Printers, Ink exhibit at our Open House party, remember? You wouldn't help me demonstrate the big presses because that was 'kid stuff,' and you were too old for it. Now this printing company of your own is kid stuff, you're willing to toss it out for junk."

"It isn't practical for John and me to go into printing on our own when the Falls Printing Company can do a better job."

"Thanks," Ed replied, and then he smiled. "Same old story. Big business gets bigger, small business gives up the unequal struggle, big business grows still bigger. All right, Hi, if you want to convert my workshop into a darkroom, go ahead."

Hi had a fifteen-year-old boy's healthy distaste for housework and Johnny had never thrown away anything in his life, but together they cleaned out the workshop in one day's time. It's true that some useful items I had been keeping handy disappeared forever into the dark maw of the attic, and it didn't seem fair that the contents of three drawers in my sewing cabinet were emptied into the bottom drawer and the top three were now dedicated to film packs and tins of chemicals and other photographic equipment. Viewing it philosophically, I decided it was wonderful that the boys were learning to be orderly. The motive might not be entirely unselfish (nor had it been when they learned to be thoughtful of others, the others being two pretty girls) but the results were a step in the right direction.

The darkroom led to more photographic equipment and eventually to the purchase of better cameras, with Ed sharing the cost on a matching-fund basis. At that point Hi approached his father once more, with a new proposition.

"I don't know how good I'll be right at first," he said, "but if you want me to take some pictures for the *Record*, I'll be glad to try. John will, too."

"I'd be very much interested," Ed replied. "I could use a couple of staff photographers."

"That wasn't exactly what we had in mind," Hi said. "We'd rather work on our own. You know, like free-lance photographers."

"What does that term mean to you?"

"You mean, 'free lance?' Well, we'll take pictures and submit them to you. If they're good enough for the paper, you take them. If they aren't, that's too bad for us."

"Let me tell you something," Ed said. "Both of you, and I want you to listen. If you question what I'm going to tell you, check with Mom. She's been a free-lance writer for seventeen, eighteen years.

"A free lance in photography, in writing, in *any* field, is free to the extent that he can go out independently, take the pictures or write the story he thinks an editor will like, but in the final analysis he can't exist 'on his own.' He has to produce what someone else wants. He has to accept correction, he has to take assignments he doesn't particularly like. In other words, he must, at some point, take orders from someone else. If he won't, if he's a prima donna, a big wheel, a temperamental cuss who rejects all ideas except his own, the chances are nine to one he'll never be much of a photographer, or much of a writer, or as a matter of fact, much of a person.

"In other words, Hi, I'm more pleased than you could know that you and John are interested in taking pictures for the *Record*, but let's understand each other. I'm the editor. Very largely because you two wanted it that way, it's *my* newspaper. You may submit any pictures you've gone out to get independently, but you must also accept assignments from me."

"We hadn't figured on doing it that way. We were going to take the pictures and let you use them if you wanted to."

"Do you want to tackle photography as professionals would, or are you just a pair of kids with a new hobby?"

"O.K., Dad." Suddenly Hi grinned boyishly. "Well, send me in, coach. Where's the first job?"

Thus the ex-partners and ex-columnists were back on the front page of the newspaper, as credit lines under news pictures. Thus our sons learned to "take orders" from Ed, not because he was their father, but because he was the editor of the newspaper in which they hoped to place their work.

The close relationship of earlier years was gone. "The four of us" was no longer the cornerstone of every project and every living day. Once we had minded the store together, bound by a struggle for survival. We were still in business for ourselves but each to his own enterprise.

Not that we were independent of each other. We lived together, we shared many goals and needs, we still liked the family plan, but now it was based on mutual interdependence, a freedom to be ourselves, a freedom to grow.

The growing, we knew, rested largely with the younger generation. How glad we are, Ed and I said to each other many times, that we don't have to go through *that* phase again. Somewhere along the line, we began to call each other by our first names, instead of "Mom" and "Dad," and as the young men turned outward to take on the whole wide world, we turned, gratefully, toward each other.

There were many signs that we had reached a new plateau, and one of them, most memorable to me because I have kept the note written by the boys, took place during a disastrous flood.

In November of 1959, warm winds combined with

heavy rainfall resulted in the worst flood in the history of the Snoqualmie Valley. Houses were damaged or swept away. Our towns were isolated from one another, hundreds of persons had to be evacuated from their homes. It was a terrifying experience, involving so many personal stories that the *Record's* pages were filled with "flood stories" for three or four editions, and of course they were busy days for the local editor.

The night the water was rising, Ed and I were late getting home. Hi and John were in bed, but they had left a note for us on the kitchen table:

> "We have gone to bed with all our
> clothes on. Also, our cameras and
> film are packed up. Wake us up
> whenever you decide to go out on
> the story. We're ready, anytime."

Their boots and waterproof jackets were on chairs beside the kitchen table. Camera cases hung from the backs of the chairs.

"Want to go out with us?" Ed asked me.

I shook my head. "No, you three go ahead. Sloshing around in floodwater at one o'clock in the morning is your department, not mine. Be careful . . ." When they left, a half hour later, I waved a sleepy farewell, and thought to myself, "Now, let's see—where *is* that hot-water bottle . . . ?"

ABOUT THE AUTHOR

CHARLOTTE PAUL was born in Seattle and spent her formative years in the Pacific Northwest. After a year of musical studies in Germany and a tour of Europe, she entered Wellesley. During college she won first prize in the Atlantic Monthly collegiate short story contest of 1937. After graduation she wrote news articles, first as assistant foreign news editor for the *Chicago Daily Times,* later as a roving correspondent for that paper in the Caribbean. Back in the United States she began a successful career of free-lance writing. Her articles and stories appear in such magazines as *The Saturday Evening Post, Esquire, Coronet, Good Housekeeping, McCall's,* and others.

Her first novel, HEAR MY HEART SPEAK, was published in 1950. GOLD MOUNTAIN, published in 1953, was a selection of the Peoples Book Club. MINDING OUR OWN BUSINESS (1955) is the heartwarming story of the experiences of the author and her husband as owners and editors of the *Snoqualmie Valley Record.* This book was also distributed by The Readers Digest Condensed Books. Her next novel, THE CUP OF STRENGTH, followed in 1958 and was taken by both the Peoples Book Club and the Family Reading Club. Most fittingly, Miss Paul received the 1957 Woman of Achievement Award from the National Federation of Press Women.

Mr. and Mrs. Groshell live in the Snoqualmie Valley, thirty miles east of Seattle. Their home stands in a meadow at the foot of 4,100-foot Mount Si of the Cascade Range. At the rear of the property is a little cedar house with a big window, where the author does her writing.

Intensely devoted to her valley region and its projects, she is also interested in a number of statewide programs, particularly the Washington State Council for Children and Youth, to which she was appointed by the Governor for a six-year term. Her husband and her two high-school-student sons, Hi and John, have always been her favorite characters and, in fact, are the heroes of her new book.